HOOLIE'S
TRUE YOOPER TALES

A look at the funny side of life
in a small mining town in the
Upper Peninsula of Michigan.

Edited by
Jesse DeCaire

ISBN-13: 978-0-9658645-3-4
ISBN-10: 0-9658645-3-7

Library of Congress Control Number: 2006923995

First Edition–2006

10 9 8 7 6 5 4 3 2 1

Published by
Yooper Innovations, Inc.
490 N. Steel St.
Ishpeming, MI 49849
1-800-628-9978

Dedicated to my mother, who was my best friend...we had a lot of good laughs together. And to my uncles Bruno, Joe, Tudy, and Frankie Sarvello, who showed me what joy there is in making people laugh.

GROWING UP IN TANGLE TOWN

PEOPLE ALWAYS used to ask my mother: "How did he get so crazy? Was he always like that? She would laugh and nod her head "yes," and while I agree with her, let me add that EVERYONE I grew up with in my neighborhood called Tangle Town, was crazier than a shit house rat. Nick Valenti, the Guru of Tangle Town, told me an alien spaceship had hovered over our neighborhood, and the exhaust from the ship was inhaled by everyone that lived in the vicinity and ever since then, no one has been quite the same. Nick was the Guru of Tangle Town. He was heavy into Red Rider comic books, and used to spend his summer days reading them over and over. We figured that anyone who took the time to read during the precious days of summer vacation had to be smart, so we believed everything he said.

Back when I was young, Ishpeming was divided into different sections and neighborhoods. Each section had its own baseball field, swimming hole, ice rink, ski hills, ma and pa stores, etc. and you didn't dare cross into anyone else's neighborhood. There was Tangle Town, Cleveland Location, Nebraska Location, Junction Location, West-end Dago Town, the West End and the Barnum Location just to name a few. Most of these neighborhoods were built around iron ore mines and most of them had tough characters, especially the

Cleveland Location. They were the biggest, toughest, meanest bunch around. I remember my buddy Bruzzy Petro had to go to the Cleveland Location once to visit his ma's sister. His Ma and Aunt kept bugging him to go out and play with the boys outside. Bruzzy knew better. There was no way in hell he was gonna go out there with that bunch of savages. Finally Bruzzy's Ma got sick of him hanging around the house so she "tossed him out to the wolves," who were outside hovering, waiting for their prey to take one step out of the house. Within minutes, they pantsed him and threw his Levis on top of a telephone pole. Then they took his underwear off and filled them up with fresh dog poop and put them back on Bruzzy. He knew he couldn't go to his ma, she wouldn't have believed him. She'd say: "If you had to take a dump, why didn't you just come in the house you pig? And I suppose you threw your pants away cause they were full of poop, eh? Take that you little weasel" (an inevitable smack).

Our neighborhood never had fighters like the others did. We'd act crazy instead and this usually helped avoid any potential fights. When we had to walk the borders of any of these locations, we'd always wear our clothes backwards and put our shoes on the wrong feet and the other kids would cross the street to avoid coming near us. They knew if you beat up a kid from Tangle Town, you would get some kind of weird curse laid upon your head. It worked too, coz I can't remember getting into a fight until I was much older…

THE BEST REALITY SHOW IN THE WORLD

EVERY NEIGHBORHOOD in town had their share of nuts, but our neighborhood had an over abundance of them, and each had their own funny peculiarities that made them so fun to live around. There was Elvin Swanson, Doc Swanson, Tea Bag Tilly, Flossy Lynn, Brucksey Lynn, Skinner Gustafson, Harold Finster, Leon Burger, Cakes Keikonen, Uncle Bruno, Soup Bone, Bunna Poleman, Bubbles Tuttala, Armest Keto, Binky Nelson, Daddy and Gary Sparks, and Peg Leg Olsen to name a few. But the craziest of them all was Springer Peterson. Springer was a 10 on a scale of crazy. Whenever he had a big project going, all us kids would be sitting around watching and waiting for him to do something crazy, so we could laugh our asses off. One time, he had to paint the eaves of his house so he borrowed my old man's wood extension ladders that were good for painting those old 2 story houses that were built around 1900. While painting, he was looking up at the eaves so he wouldn't miss a spot, but the problem was he had real drippy paint so he was getting splattered pretty good. He'd come down the ladder with his face speckled white and his glasses even worse, and wipe them off with a rag full of gas. Once back up under the eaves, as soon as he'd make a couple of strokes, the paint would start dripping all over his face again. Within moments he was back down the ladder wiping his face and glasses with gas. After it happened a third time, he started swearing and muttering: "Why you no good for nothing rotten bugger… I'll fix you…" and dunked his brush into the can of paint and started painting his whole face white! It was great! Springer just kept painting the eaves and every once in a while when he got splattered he'd go over his face to keep the paint uniform. I don't know how he ever saw what he was doing coz his glasses were coated with the paint too…

Springer loved to paint things. In fact, he was into anything that had to do with the upkeep of his house, almost obsessively: gardening, pruning, mowing, you name it. One day, he was painting his '52 Chevy with a can of black paint and a paintbrush. When he finished one side he'd step back to admire his nice paint job, and just like it was on cue, the wind kicked up and plastered leaves, sticks and sand all over his fresh paint job. Springer whiffed the brush at the car and jumped up and down yelling over and over: "Shit, shit, shit, shit, why me?" When he finally calmed down, he started picking the leaves and sticks off the car and re-painted that side. When he stepped back to admire his touch up job, the wind once again kicked up and blew more leaves, twigs, bugs, and sand all over the wet paint. Holy wah, Springer chucked the paint brush over the roof of the house, started kicking the ground, jumping up and down and calling God all kinds of names. After that, he went into the house, only to emerge an hour later, where he started to pick the leaves and twigs and bugs off the car. He then resumed painting the car, this time doing the whole car in one fail swoop. When he finished and stepped back to admire his paint job, wouldn't you know it the wind blew a swift gust and blew all matters of dead caterpillars, sand, leaves and twigs once again all over his car, this time covering the whole car. Springer turned beet red. He punted his brush into Sodergren's yard next door, said one cuss word which I won't repeat here, and then grabbed a shovel from the garage and started firing shovelfuls of sand, dirt, grass, and night crawlers all over his car.

He drove around in that Chevy with all that crap stuck to it, for years. We thought it looked cool as hell. Camouflage by Springer Peterson.

Springer kept his yard immaculate… nothing was out of place. I think he even combed his grass with a hairbrush. We came up with a plan to see if we could get a charge out of him. We took a rock about the size of a soft ball and tossed it over the fence into his yard, and then found a hiding place to wait for Springer to come out and check his yard. Eventually he came out and took a look around and saw the rock lying there. He went over and stared at it for awhile, then looked up at the sky like that's where it fell from, and then picked it up and heaved it over the fence into the alley. Once he left and went into his barn, we grabbed the rock and flung it back into his yard. When he came out and spotted the rock laying in his yard again, he muttered something to himself, picked it up, looked up at the sky again, came out to the alley and looked around and seeing that there was no one there, he chucked it down the alley and went into the house. We came out of hiding, and tossed the rock back into his yard again. About 15 minutes later, Springer came out the house and spotted the rock. By now he was pissed… he was muttering and swearing and shaking his fist at the sky. He went over to his barn and got a shovel out, and started digging a 3-foot deep hole in the alleyway. Then he grabbed the rock and dropped it in and filled in the hole, jumping up and down on it when it was full for good measure. We waited until he got into the house to burst out laughing. Springer was a real character… they just don't make 'em like him anymore.

But, Springer wasn't the only character around. One day, me and my best friend Vito were walking by Harold Finster's house. Harold's old man had built a 7-foot plank fence around the house, and Blinky Nelson told us he built it to keep Harold and his sister Lu-Lu in when the full moon came out. Anyhow, we could hear Harold on the other side of the fence saying over and over: "7-7-7-7-7-7-7-7-7...." We looked at each other like, "What the hell is going on?"

So I told Vito: "Take a look through that knot hole in the fence and see what's going on in there." Vito bent over to take a look and a finger came out and poked him in the eyeball.

We hear soon after, Harold squeal with delight, "8-8-8-8-8-8-8-8-8...."

I remember my ma telling me not to hang around Cakes Keikonen cause he was odd. I didn't quite understand what she meant coz hell, everyone in the neighborhood was odd. Well, after bugging her over and over, ma finally told me she didn't want me around Cakes coz he was a fairy. I thought that was a little strange coz I had just went swimming with Cakes the other day and I didn't see any wings. Maybe they were invisible or something. Anyway, him and Bubbles Tutola went up on Jackson Bluff all the time together and one day I saw Bubbles and asked if he had fun with Cakes up there and he replied, "Weeeeeeeee...."

Our neighborhood was the best reality show in the world... free entertainment everyday. Boy do I miss those carefree days when people like Springer had us in stitches. It seems that nowadays people take themselves too seriously. We need to slow down and learn to laugh at life a little more. We're all too busy and wrapped up in our own lives that we don't enjoy the simple pleasures of our neighbors. If we can break out of our private shells, trust me, it'll sure beat an episode of "Survivor" any day.

Doug Trebilcock, Hoolie, Jeff Jensen

Hoolie, Vito Carello, Etta Norman

Etta, Jeff, Hoolie, My sister Doe Doe

Cousins Jo Jo Valente, Butch Sarvello, Hoolie

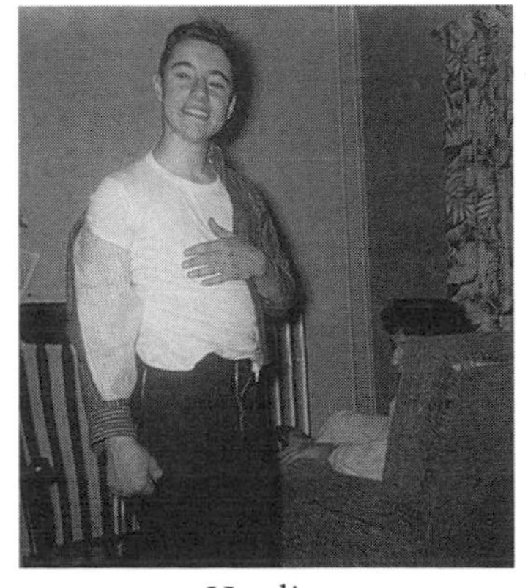
Hoolie

Da Italian Cousins

STEP RIGHT UP!

Fergie Aho was out prowling for men at Woody's Bar. She eventually meets Chick Mehan who was a stud from Tangle Town if there ever was one. They talk, they connect, and at the end of the night they leave together. Chick takes her back to his place and shows her around his apartment. When they get to his bedroom, it's packed to the gills with sweet cuddly teddy bears. Hundreds of cute small bears on a low shelf and all along the floor, adorable medium sized ones on another shelf higher up, and huge enormous bears on the very highest shelf.

Fergie was surprised to say the least. She couldn't believe that a man would have such an extensive collection of teddy bears, but she just let it slide, after all he was a very good looking guy, and to tell the truth, she was a little impressed that he had a sensitive side to him. She turns to him and in an instant they are kissing and ripping each other's clothes off and within 15 minutes are making hot steamy love.

After an intense night of passion, they are lying on Chick's bed in the afterglow, her thoroughly pleased with her sensitive lover, when she rolls over and asks him smiling, "Well how was it?"

Chick replies, "You can choose any prize you like from the bottom shelf."

THE LITTLE RED WAGON

I was walking in the neighborhood one day when I see Bunna Poleman's kid Jeffery riding in a little red wagon pulled by his dog Humphrey. He had one end of the rope tied to the wagon handle and the other end attached to Humphrey's nuts.

"You know," I said to him as I passed by, "If you tie the rope around his neck, it would probably go faster."

"I know." Jeffery replies, "but then I wouldn't get the cool siren."

WINTER ENTERTAINMENT

BECAUSE WE had no TV in the 50's, we had to find other ways to entertain ourselves in the winter. No one stayed in the house unless you were so sick you couldn't move. We had a huge cardboard slide down the street that we rode constantly, the Ishpeming Ice Rink where we spent most of winter, sleigh riding on John Pete's hill, and the ski jumps on the neighborhood hills. Every neighborhood had ski jump hills. Ours had: Tree Gap, Short Stop, Daisy, Rocky, and Brass Wire.

On weekends we shacked cars. The road was always slick with snow and ice so this was considered cheap transportation and fun winter entertainment. The best boots for shacking cars were ski boots; they slid the best on ice and snow. Leather choppers were great for the hands, coz they didn't stick to the bumpers like woolen mittens did. Every winter, thousands of mittens clung to the bumpers of cars. Sometimes if you were lucky you shacked a car that had your mittens you lost last week still stuck to them.

Me and Vito used to hide in the snow bank by Charlie Richard's store and wait for cars to drive up so we could shack them. One time, Sula Ristanen, one of the town drunks stopped in front of the store to buy some jumbos. When she came back out, we jumped on the back bumper. Instead of going forward, she accidentally put it in reverse, rolled and stopped on one of Vito's new ski boots. Then she put it in drive and burned rubber, tearing Vito's boots into sixty-two pieces. Boy did he catch hell when he got home.

My crowning achievement though was the time me and Vito were heading out to the Winter Sports area to do some downhill skiing. It was a two-mile walk so hell, why walk when we could shack a car? So with our skis over our shoulders, we caught this car at the end of 3rd Street by the Baptist Church. We were about a half-mile from approaching US Highway 41, when the car got the green light to go. By this time it was going about forty miles an hour, and we were on back enjoying the rush we felt from shacking so long, so much so that we forgot a very important detail: the highway was always free and clear of ice and snow. Once we hit that bare pavement, we rolled about thirty feet, ass over tin cups and tore the hell out of our bums and had to limp the last half mile to the ski hill. In the end, we hung on all nine blocks of 3rd street... I think we still hold the record today for the longest shack job in Ishpeming...

TARZAN SWING

ME, VITO, and Jeffrey Jensen had a Tarzan swing that swung over a fifty-foot cliff by my house. You didn't dare let go or you ended up on a pile of scrap iron, railroad ties, and pugle stakes at the bottom of the cliff.

One day, the neighborhood bully, Eyeballs Jackson was coming down the tracks that led to our swing. We knew he was going to move in on our swing and start pushing us around like he always did. This time though, we were ready for him. We loosened the knot at the top of the swing that attached it to the tree and waited. Sure as hell, he came over and started pushing us around and telling us that he was going to swing on our swing. We told him he couldn't coz he was too big, he'd break it. But like we figured, that only enticed him more. Shoving me out of the way, he grabbed the swing and took a running leap and swung out over the cliff, and as if we couldn't have planned it better, the rope let loose while he was fully extended over the drop off. All three of us cringed when he hit that scrap pile and rolled down it... we'd never seen anyone take a fall like that! Once we saw some movement from Eyeballs, we yelled to him:

"WE TOLD YOU SO! WE TOLD YOU IT'D BREAK!" Eyeballs continued to lie there, bleeding and bruised, his pride hurting more than his ass. Then on cue I started crying "MA, MA, MA HE BROKE OUR SWING! EYEBALLS JACKSON BROKE OUR SWING!" That got him up. Once he limped far enough out of earshot, we laughed our asses off. Nothing was greater than getting even with a guy that tormented the little guys. We were heroes of the neighborhood for weeks.

DOG BISCUIT

This blind man I used to know was standing on a street corner in downtown Newberry with his Seeing-Eye Dog. As they were standing there waiting for the streetlight to change, the dog lifted his leg and peed on the guy's pant leg. The man then reached into his pocket and took out a dog biscuit and gave it to the dog. Elmer Aho, who had been watching this, ran up to the blind man and said,

"You shouldn't do that you know. He'll never learn anything if you reward him when he does something like that!"

"Oh I'm not rewarding him." The blind guy retorted, "I'm just trying to find his head so that I can kick him in the ass!"

THE PRIDE OF THE NORTH

In South Carolina, a young boy is attacked by a bear while walking home from school. A passerby sees the drama and pulls his car over to help out. The stranger grabs the bear off the boy and chokes it to death with his bare hands, saving the boy's life.

While all this was happening, the editor of the local newspaper happened to drive by. He was absolutely thrilled to have witnessed such an act of heroism, that he told the man who choked the bear, that his name was going to be on the front page of the next day's edition. The headline would read, "South Carolina Man Heroically Saves Boy's Life."

The man replies after the editor is finished, "That's wonderful, but I'm not from South Carolina."

"Fine," the editor says, "How about 'Southern Man Heroically Saves Boy's Life?"

"That's fine, but I'm not from the South either," says the man.

"Okay, where are you from then?" Asks the editor. The man explains that he's a Yooper from Upper Michigan.

The next day, the front page of the paper reads: "Deranged Yankee Kills Family Pet."

"HARK I HEARD A SHITSAL POT, HARK I HEAR A..." MY FIRST TIME ON STAGE

I COULD never grasp the intracacies of the English language... in other words, I can't write or spell. Memorizing has never been a strong point of mine either. You see, I was hit in the head with a baseball at the early age of 9 and ever since then I've had trouble keeping things in my head. This makes life difficult sometimes. Like the time my 6th grade teacher Miss Tucker was putting together a play for our class to perform. Despite my protests, I was given a part where I had to come out and speak one line: "Hark! I heard a Pistol Shot!"

I went home and told my Ma that I got a speaking part in the play, but that I was too dumb to do it, and while she agreed with me, she told me to go for it coz she wanted to see her son up there on the stage. So it was settled. For the next two weeks before the play I worked my ass off memorizing that line. "Hark! I heard a pistol Shot! Hark I heard a pistol shot!" Over and over again, walking around the house, in my room, at the dinner table... and my old man got so sick of me repeating that line, that he went out to camp and stayed there until the play was over. Finally, the night of the play I was shitting my pants nervous. I couldn't even remember my own name let alone that one line. I had to have Miss Tucker remind me right before I went out, and when the moment came, the gunshot went off, she had to give me a good shove to get on stage. I was frozen in terror. My mind blanked. When I finally opened my mouth, this is what came out:

"Hark! I heard a shitsal pot. No, No, No, I mean Hark! I heard Pristal Spot. Hark! I heard… oh shit on it. I didn't want to be in this bloody play anyways," and turned and walked off the stage. So much for my big stage debut. At least I got the biggest laugh of the night. All the dudes in my class thought it was awesome, so for like a week after that I was their hero. I ended up doing a few more plays in high school but it was all characters that never spoke a line. I wonder why that was?

THE SLOW BUNCH

I WAS a D student in high school, so I got stuck in the classes that had all the criminals, flunkies, hoods and students that were in their thirties. I didn't fall into any of these categories, but being the "Class Clown" and supplying all the sound effects that would disrupt the class was enough of a qualification to get me into these elite classes. I always figured I wasn't learning anything so why should anyone else? My old man could see I wasn't gonna be the sharpest tool in the woodshed, and I remember once he took me down the basement and showed me two shovels. He said as he pointed to one of the shovels:

"That one there is a coal shovel. It's for shoveling coal and snow. The other one with the big handle is a muck stick I borrowed from the mine. We use that one for shoveling muck and it's also good for turning' over dirt in the garden. Pick 'em up and get the feel of them... coz at the rate your goin' in school, you're gonna be at the end of one of them for the rest of your life."

One good thing that came out of being in the Slow Bunch was I got to know all the weirdoes that couldn't conform and all the tough guys who carried knives and brass knuckles that could fight like hell. If anyone tried picking on me from any of the neighborhoods, I'd tell them I was going to visit my buddy

Zorro (one of the tough guys) and they'd back off. I loved the guys and girls in those classes, we shared that special bond that only comes between people who weren't quite able to fit in with everyone else and wouldn't you know it? Most of them ended up Presidents, Owners and Bosses of some of the biggest companies in the country.

THE GUNGA DINS

"Where dat damn Gunga Din wit dat water?
Fetch me some water, Din, I need a drink
Hurry fast coz dose crazy La Mumba Gunks are coming at us again!"
-Din Da Water Boy, IHS 1963

I FORMED the Gunga Dins in 1959 when I was a freshman doing time at ol' Ishpeming High School. That place was a strict no nonsense, toe the mark, keep your mouth shut school prison system. It was the perfect place for a guy like me with my D average, fool around, rebellious, trouble-making, disrupt the class, clown persona. I was fortunate to be put in classes with 35 year old draft dodgers, thieves, crooks, hoodlums, screwed up rich kids, and brainless wonders who all had D averages and didn't give a shit. The jailers that tried to teach us were mean and tough and didn't think twice about kicking your ass if you got out of line. If you could pull something off on these guys you were treated good by the rest of the convicts in your class and the word spread around that you were an OK dude.

One day, Zorro Zalic told me I should form a resistance group, a secret organization that would resist and disrupt at a more organized level... you know like forge hall passes and sick day excuses, doctors appointments and funeral leave. It was a great idea! So a day later, The Gunga Dins was formed. Meetings were held in the library under the guise of the "Ishpeming High School Reading Club." We had 12 main leaders or Dins as they were called, who were all freshman, and each Din had their own pack from their neighborhoods: Salsbury, Cleveland Location, Lake Bancroft, Tangle Town, Humboldt, Diorite, Junction, Barnum, Nebraska, West end Dago Town, Lake Angeline, Deer Lake, and the 8th Edition. Organized like that, The Gunga Dins accomplished some great feats. Once we carried a VW into the school and put it in the main hall just before first bell. Another time we got up on the roof of the school and bombarded the teachers with water balloons when they came up to the main door. We hid in the school one night and turned the pool water down to just above freezing. That was a good one because all the guys who swam the next day froze their bums off and their family jewels shrunk up pretty bad.

The warden got wind of our secret organization when some of the guys from the sophomore class got locked in their lockers all day. The little weasels turned in some of our members and told the warden they were Gunga Dins. Shortly after that episode the sophomores formed their own organization called La Mumba Gunks. We always had a sneaking suspicion that these guys were working directly with the warden gathering information because soon after their formation, our meetings of the IHS Reading Club were tossed out of the library for good. And with that, the Cold War between us and them began. Spies were everywhere. We couldn't get anything started without one of the jailers coming into the boys' toilet and breaking up our meetings or tossing us out of the basketball games because someone lit off a stink bomb.

We knew something had to be done about La Mumba Gunks. Most of La Mumba Gunk guys were going with girls from our class, so we played hardball and invited the toughest women in our class to be honorary members of the Gunga

Dins. My girl buddy Fran, who was 6' 2" and could play frontline for the Packers, organized the girls into a dating spy network that kept track of the top leaders of La Mumba Gunks. Through them, we would find out where those guys were at all times so we could blame them for things we did. One time, Fran got a bunch of bloomers from the Salvation Army and decorated the main school hallway with them. She wrote all the top leader's from La Mumba Gunks names in them and what girls that they took them off. Of course Fran put down all the cheerleaders names and the stuck up babes she hated. They caught hell for that one.

I had a lot of fun and laughs with those guys in the Gunga Dins Society. We were misfits and outsiders that didn't quite fit in... the underdogs that gravitated toward each other. Most of them ended up coming back to Ishpeming and stopping in at the Tourist Trap to visit with old Hoolie again: The Butler Brothers, Dick Sharland, Eddy V, Bobby "Zorro" Zalic, Vito, Dave Delongchamp and all the rest of the crazy buggers. I hope things are going good for youse guys. And Fran, get a hold of me and we'll go and get all buzzed up on peach and honey again like we used to, eh.

GUNGA DINS FOREVER.

PLUCK YOU!

Before the Battle of Agincount in 1415, the French, anticipating victory over the English, proceeded to cut off the middle finger of all captured English soldiers. Without the middle finger, it would be impossible to draw the renowned English Longbow and therefore be incapable of fighting in the future.

This famous weapon was made of the native English Yew Tree and the act of drawing the Longbow was known as "Plucking the Yew." Much to the bewilderment of the French, the English won a major upset and began mocking the French by waving their middle fingers at the defeated French saying, "See we can still pluck Yew! PLUCK YEW!" Since "Pluck Yew" is rather difficult to say, the difficult consonant cluster at the beginning has gradually changed to an "F." Thus the words often used in conjuction with the "one finger salute" are mistakenly thought to have something to do with an intimate encounter between two people. It is also because of the pheasant feathers on the arrows used with the Longbow that the symbolic gesture is known as "Giving the Bird."

And Yew thought Yew knew everything.

THE ISHPEMING GARLIC SNAPPERS

OUR FOOTBALL team was called the Ishpeming Garlic Snappers. We were a scrappy bunch of guys. Karly Jackson, who was our quarterback, was 5'2" and wore coke bottle glasses (he couldn't see nothing). Our fullback was "Bugeyes" Johnson who was the tallest guy on the team at 6'1", 97 lbs. soaking wet, and had one leg that was shorter than the other. The two-backfield guys were brothers, Cuff and Link Nelson, who were small but boy were they tough. They were great to give the ball to because neither one of them ever took a bath, so no one on the other team would go near them. Then there was this Italian guy on the team named Jo Jo Valenti who always ate garlic. His farts and breath would peel the skin off a dog at a hundred paces. No one on the other team wanted to play across from him coz he would breathe on them and constantly fart during the game. That gave us an idea. We figured, since we couldn't play worth a shit, if the whole team ate garlic before each game, maybe we could fart like Jo and "gas" the other team to the verge of retching, and force them to forfeit the game.

So that's what we did. We got to be known as the "Ishpeming Garlic Snappers." Every time we lined up for a play, the other team would line up five yards away from us. Even though this gained us five yards a carry, we were still unable to win a game, but it sure beat the hell out of getting flattened every play. The other team was always afraid to pile on us in case one of us farted in the pile. They would just knock us down and run away. I know it sounds ridiculous, but hell, at least it gave us some kind of advantage over those other teams!

Hoolie's dad, hard day at da mine

Two young French men,
Hoolie's dad Suma
& Tubeach Carkin

A young Italian girl,
Hoolie's mom Mary

Mary with Hoolie's daughter -
Anna 1969

Hoolie's family 1950's

Hoolie & Doe-Doe in front of -
Mary's community Christmas tree

GOOD OLD FASHION RESPECT

I WAS at Snyder's Drug Store in Ishpeming picking up some foot powder when I ran into one of the old Ishpeming High School teachers who's now retired, Mr. Carylson. We were talking and having some laughs, when suddenly this familiar feeling came back to me... a feeling I hadn't had since talking to him in the halls of IHS when I was younger: a guilty nervous twitch like I had done something wrong. After awhile we shook hands and said goodbye and as his car pulled out onto Highway 41, I thought how strange that not only after all these years I felt that strange guilty feeling that only comes in the presence of authority figures, but here I am 60 years old and I still call him "Mr. Carylson." It's funny how I never lost that respect I had for people older than me. I think my parents instilled that. For example, my Old Man gave everybody that was older than me unwritten permission to kick my ass if I got out of line (boy did they ever take advantage of that!). Sometimes I deserved it, sometimes I didn't, but I always prayed like hell my dad didn't find out about it coz, I would get it again from him, guilty or not. He was an underground miner so he could throw me through two rooms of the house without any part of my body touching the rug. If my criminal buddies were up to no good like robbing somebody or wrecking something, they always dropped me off somewhere before they went out coz none of 'em wanted to face my Old Man if we got caught. They feared him more than they feared the cops. They would never come into the house and if they accidentally ran into him in the backyard they put their heads down and called him "Mr. DeCaire." Now, coming from those thieves and fighters, that's what you call good old fashion respect!

Both my parents came from very strict upbringing and they brought us up the same way. Never talk back to your elders. Never raise your voice to your mother. And you did what you were told to do. Once was enough, and if they had to tell you a second time you were in trouble. Along with this strict upbringing, my parents came from humble backgrounds. They were working people and sometimes had to deal with the reality of prejudices. They taught us that people are the same whether you're rich, poor, black, white, red, yellow, brown, etc. They told us not to make fun of people if they were overweight or looked funny. Be their friend coz it will be the best friend you ever had. In turn we brought our kids up the same way and they all turned out to be very kind and considerate people. What's going wrong today? I don't know, but I think the world could learn a little from these old timers.

NEW SUIT

Burt Neimi was moderately successful in his career as a Mine Boss at CCI. But as he got older, he found it harder and harder to go to work because of these incredible headaches he was getting. It was when his personal life started to suffer though when he decided to finally seek medical help. After being referred from one specialist to another down in Marquette, he finally came across a doctor who solved the problem. His name was Dr. Ali Jem Leery.

"The good news is I can cure your headaches," said Doc Leery. "The bad news is it will require castration. You have a very rare condition that causes your testicles to press up against the base of your spine. The pressure on the spine is what's creating your bad headaches, and the only way to relieve this pressure is to remove your testicles." Bert was shocked and depressed. After pleading with the doctor to find another way and seeking unsuccessful second opinions, and with his headaches still making it impossible for him to concentrate, Bert decided to go through with the operation.

Having got the surgery, his mind was finally clear and free of pain. He felt like a different person. He felt like making a new beginning in his life, and as he passed a men's clothing store he thought: "That's what I need! A new suit!" He walked into the store and up to the clerk and said, "I'd like a new suit please."

The salesman eyed him briefly and said, "Let's see, Size 44 long."

Bert laughed. "That's right! How did you know that?"

"It's my job to know that, sir." the clerk replied. Bert tried on the suit. It fit perfectly. As he admired himself in the mirror, the salesman asked, "How about a new shirt?" Bert thought for a moment and agreed with the salesman. "Let's see-34 sleeve, 16 1/2 neck."

Bert was surprised. "How did you know that?"

"It's my job sir." Bert tried on the shirt and it fit perfectly. As Bert was adjusting his collar in the mirror the clerk asked,

"How about some new shoes?" Well, Bert thought, might as well, I'm on a roll. The salesman eyed Bert's feet and said "Let's see, 9 1/2 wide."

Bert was astonished. "How do you know all this stuff?"

"Sir, it's my job to know." Bert tried the shoes on and they fit perfectly. As he was walking around confidently in his new attire, the salesman piped up, "How about a new hat?" Without hesitating, Bert agreed. "Let's see-7 5/8."

Bert couldn't believe it. "But how did you know?"

"It's my job to know sir." The clerk said nonchalantly. The hat fit perfectly and was the perfect addition to his new duds. Bert was feeling great. After he did some strutting around, the salesman asked, "How about some new underwear?" Bert pondered for a moment then said,

"What the heck, sure." The salesman eyed Bert's waist.

"Let's see—-size 36."

Bert laughed. "No you finally got one wrong! I've worn size 34 since I was 18 years old!"

The salesman shook his head. "There's no way you wear a size 34. If you did, it would press your testicles up against the base of your spine and give you a horrible headache!"

DATING IN THE 50'S AND 60'S

GETTING A date in Ishpeming in the 1950's was bleak. If you tried to date a woman from another location like Champion or Barnum, the guys would show no mercy. If they caught you with one of their women they would either kick your ass or stone you out of their neighborhood. It must have been like that in Negaunee too, because the Negaunee dudes use to come to Ishpeming to burn, pillage, and steal our women. Because of this, we came to an unwritten understanding with Negaunee that no one would get their asses kicked if we dated each other's women. It was a good thing too, coz all of us in my neighborhood were getting sick of our dates ending with us running while rocks hit us in the back of the head. You see, none of us were fighters so we had to instead learn to run fast, and as a result of this, most of Ishpeming's best track stars came out of our neighborhood. We never got any dates but boy could we run.

When I think back to those days, it seemed that most of the guys and girls dated people from other towns. It was like it was more exotic to date someone from another town I guess. When I was in high school we use to go out and stay at friends camps out in Lake Michigamme and go to the dances up there. Ronnie Neff had a boat so we use to get up real early and hit all the boats parked in front of other camps and steal enough gas to go to those dances. Man, they had some great looking women up there. Lots of guys from Ishpeming ended up marrying women from Michigamme.

When I turned 18, I hit the road with my band that included Ernie Brown, Jim Meyskins, and "Wild" Bill Morcom. The first place we played back in 1964 was a college joint full of students, bikers, homosexuals, crazies, and the like. Coming out of Ishpeming the boys and I got a real fast education on the ways of the world. I was sitting at the bar between sets when a gorgeous woman called me over to her table. She told me to sit down and talk, so I complied. She told me she really liked drummers and I told her that I liked anyone who liked drummers. Things continued in that vein until soon enough I felt a tap on my shoulder. Standing behind me was this huge behemoth of a biker woman that was built and looked like a man. She told me to get the hell out of her chair, that was her woman I was talking to. I guess she didn't like drummers.

We had a hell of a good time playing and the women seemed to come easier when you were in a band. Some of the backwater towns we played in had never seen a live rock band before, so these women were all over us like we were the Beatles or something. We all stayed single though, because back then going steady with someone was like being married and you couldn't do anything without your woman finding out. If you were dating a Negaunee girl and she found out that you were messing around, she'd call you all kinds of bad names that would make sailors jealous, and then beat the hell out of you.

In the end though, I was fortunate to marry a great woman from Palmer. She could out drink and out fight any of my buddies so they were really jealous of me. My advice to young guys now-a-days is don't get married 'til you find a woman that is a great friend and lots of fun to hang with coz in the long run looks don't mean a thing.

THE '47 CHEVY

WHEN WE first got our band together back in 1964, we used to haul our gear around in "Wild" Bill Morcom's 1947 Chevy. That car was a classic. The Ishpeming police used to borrow it to train their new rookies in finding the fifty-seven defects the car had. It had a bent frame, so when you drove it down the road, you looked out the driver side window instead of the windshield, which had a big crack in it so you couldn't see out of it anyway. There were big holes in the floor of the back seat so if nature called, all you had do is to piss in these holes onto the highway. One front fender was gone, so we only had one light (the lights were on the fenders) and that had a short in it so it only worked when we could afford fuses. The front passenger door was tied shut coz the door handle fell off and the drivers side door was bent from hitting a tree and wouldn't open so we had to crawl through the window to get out. Both the plastic covers of the taillights were broken, so we taped red plastic reflectors over them that we found on a railroad sign. It had no heater and the tires were so bald you could see the air in them.

Boy did we have fun in that car. Like the time me and Billy took two women from Suomi out on a date. Now, when I was in high school, dates were as scarce as alligators in the U.P, so after great efforts, I lined me and "Wild" Bill Morcom up with two beauties from Suomi. We took them to the movies then to Norpees for pizza. On the way back to Suomi, we pulled into the Palmer Dump to do some necking.

We had "Wild" Bill's '47 Chevy, and being that it was the middle of winter (when isn't it the middle of winter up here?) we had blankets to keep us warm. "Wild" Bill was in the back wrapped up in a blanket with his date and I was in the front with mine talking about school when all of a sudden "Wild" Bill leaves the loudest fart I've ever heard. Talk about embarrassing. With the mood successfully ruined, I started the car and headed for Suomi to drop the girls off. It was silent the whole way. On the way home I laid into Bill. "What the hell do you gotta embarrass us in front of those two beautiful women for?"

"What are you talking about?" He asked.

"Did you have to leave that big fart? Jesus, I can't take you anywhere without you pulling some kind of shit like that. Now we're never going to get a date with them again!"

"That fart? It wasn't me, it was my date! Swear to god. It's a good thing you left right after that, coz I could hardly breathe under that blanket it stunk so bad."

I was impressed. That's the kind of date a Yooper guy loves. One who farts on the first date, eh.

A YOOPER CONTEMPLATES MARRIAGE

THERE ARE certain attributes that a Yooper guy looks for in a woman when he decides to give up the single life and get hitched. Can she rebuild a pickup truck motor? Does she know how to run and maintain a snow blower? When you fart does she give you a high five sign and say good one? Will she help you hoist up your buck on a buck pole without complaining? You don't want one like the women on those exercise commercials that look like they are on steroids, but she's gotta have enough muscle to help you on the other end of the transmission she's putting in the pickup for you. When you get married, your buddies understand what's up... they don't laugh at the fact that your new wife has a mustache. In fact, they're all envious of you because she can out drink and out fight all of them!

When I married my wife, she had a better job than I had. I didn't feel lowly because she owned a snow machine and I couldn't afford one. I didn't feel inferior because she had a new pickup with a camper on the back and a trailer with an 18-foot boat for fishing. I didn't feel degraded cause she owned two ATV 4 wheelers and I couldn't even afford one. Hell, I married her and boy, were the guys jealous! She loves the new snow blower I got her for Christmas. Now she doesn't have to shovel and scoop the snow. We're putting on an extra large garage in back so she can pull maintenance on the vehicles inside instead of freezing her buns off outside. I can live with the satisfaction that no one ever said I was a tight ass with my wife's money.

It was our 40th wedding anniversary Saturday and I thought we should do something romantic for this one… you know, go out and eat, drink and dance the night away. So we searched "The Mining Journal" to see where the biggest wedding reception was. We found one at the Ishpeming Armory. Hell, we walked in bearing a gift for the bride and groom, and they didn't have a clue if we were related, they just shook our hands and smiled. Boy, what a wedding! Free food! Free drinks! A good polka band and lots of fights! What more could a Yooper couple ask for on their anniversary, eh?

So there you go… 40 years and still cooking. Take it from Hoolie, that stuff you do in the back seat of the Chevy with the girlfriend doesn't last long...when you get married, make sure you married one like I did!

THE SUNKEN VESSEL

U-Bolt and Eye Bolt Carylson were identical twins. U-Bolt owned an old dilapidated boat and kept pretty much to himself. One day, he rented out his boat to a group of Trolls from down below who ended up sinking it. He spent all day trying to salvage as much stuff as he could from the sunken vessel and was out of touch most of the day and evening. Unbeknownst to him, his brother Eye Bolt's wife died suddenly in his absence.

When he got back on shore, he went into town to pick up a few things at the IGA Grocery Store. He ran into Bertha Anderson, an old lady from town, who mistook him for Eye Bolt and said, "I'm sorry for your loss. You must feel terrible." U-Bolt, thinking Bertha was talking about his boat said,

"Hell no! Actually, I'm sort of glad to be rid of her. She was a rotten old thing from the beginning. Her bottom was all shriveled up and she smelled like old dead fish. She was always holding water. She had a bad crack in the back and a pretty big hole in the front too. Every time I used her, her hole got bigger and she leaked like crazy. I guess what finally finished her off was when I rented her out to those four "Apple Knockers" looking for a good time. I warned them that she wasn't very good and that she smelled bad but they wanted her anyway. The damn bloody fools tried to get in her all at one time and she split right up the middle."

Old Lady Anderson couldn't believe her ears and fainted right on the spot.

GONE FISHING

One afternoon, two worms, Mutti and Janice, were crawling through the grass. Mutti says to Janice, "How about if you and I go back to your place?"

"That sounds like a good idea," Janice replies. So they inch their way back to her place and once they are there, Mutti notices that Janice is wearing a wedding ring.

"I'm sorry, Honey," Mutti says, "I don't do this kinda stuff with married worms."

"Don't worry," Janice says reassuringly, "My husband is not coming home."

"How do you know that for sure?" Mutti asks.

"Well, he got up early this morning and went fishing."

FREDRIC'S OF IRONWOOD

Dicky Bird's wife decided she wanted to do something special to please her man when he came home from his hunting trip. So she decided to buy a pair of crotchless panties from the Fredric's of Ironwood catalog. That night when he got home, Dicky walked into the bedroom to find his wife sprawled on the bed spread eagle.

"Hi Honey," she purred in a seductive voice. "Come and get some of this!"

"God no!" Roared Dickey. "Look at what it did to your undies!"

HOW DRUMMING KEPT ME OUT OF VIETNAM

THE WAR in Viet Nam was heating up and I knew I was going to get drafted, so I went down to the Royal and asked all the Vets what I should do. They told me not to sign up voluntarily to just take the Draft that way I could go in now and get the 2 years over with and not worry about any extended period. So that's what I did. It worked out great too because there was a group of guys from Ishpeming that I knew going in at the same time. Before I left, the Vets gave me some good advice that worked both in and out of the Army: "Don't volunteer for anything," and "Keep your big mouth shut and play the game and you'll survive." I still repeat those words today.

The year was 1965. There was a long period of peace, so most of the Drill Sergeants that were still in the service were lifers from WWII and the Korean War serving out their 20-year stints. They were getting used to their "Beetle Bailey" lifestyle: small, all volunteer companies and no pressure. Then here comes the largest draft since WWII full of us gomers, hippies, criminals, and guys who dropped out of college, guys who didn't want to be there, to infringe on their easy lifestyle. The day we stepped off the bus at that army training sight for basic training, those DI's kicked the shit out of our dumb asses. They were on us like flies on shit.

"Eh boy what are you using that fork for?" They would say. "Throw it away and eat with your hands! You're nothing but an animal now!" And, "Troop, you're nothing but a lazy fat ass! Run! Run! Run!" Me being a Yooper, I was used to that though, coz that's how the boss at work always talked to me anyway.

It didn't take long for my trouble making side to come out though. Soon after I got settled into the routine of Army life, I got 4 other guys together, one from every company to start looking into the most effective ways to cause trouble. We got a hold of some army manuals, the Bibles of the Army, to do some research to find any loophole we could find. For instance, the DI's weren't allowed to use foul language to get a point across. So the next time the DI used "foul" language (which was usually every other word) we went to the Chaplain and complained that we were Christians who never used the "F" word in our lives. We caught hell for that one. The head redneck DI screamed at us when he saw us again. "You bunch of babies! Go run to the preacher when you hear a few cuss words... You're all a bunch of babies, aren't you?"

"Yes, Sergeant!" We'd yell.

"You all wanna go home to your nice little bedrooms and have Mommy tuck you in at night, don't you?"

"Yes Sergeant, We wanna go home!"

"Shut up you bunch of Yellow Belly Cream Puff Ma-Ma's Boys! I'd like to put you all in a bus and send you home!"

"Yes, send us home Sergeant!"

"Shut up you bunch of Commie Hippies! Go to the Chaplain like a bunch of crybabies. That's what you are, cry babies!

"Yeah, we're all cry babies, and wanna go home to our Mudders!" We'd reply. When they got all 300 of us to stop shouting, they lined us up and marched us to this big wooden deserted building.

At this point, I'm thinking, "What did I get these guys into? Me and my big mouth!" We all got inside and the DI's locked all the doors and posted someone outside each door. The head DI gets up and starts shouting again, but this time, he looks like he wants to kill us.

"Ok you bunch of pansy asses! You wanna cry for your Mama's now? You gonna turn us in to the Preacher Man again? Coz I will personally beat the crap out of you one at a time... Are you boys gonna let us turn you into soldiers or are you gonna continue to irritate the shit out of me?"

"No, Sargent!" We said in unison.

"Are you boys ready to be killing machines?"

"Yes, Sergeant!"

"Are you gonna shut your pie holes and become American fighting men?"

"Yes, Sergeant!" We'd yell.

That night we had a meeting of the "Big Four" and I came up with a plan to get the DI's off our back. It was called the "Gung Ho Plan," and we spread it through the entire company. The next day at bayonet training we had to learn to thrust and perry with this stabbing dummy that was set up. I made sure I was first in line so the guys could take their cue from me. Right before I went, I started growling and snapping my teeth and digging my feet in. Then the Sergeant yelled: "You're a lean, mean fighting machine! Go kill that Commie Bastard!"

I let out this blood-curdling scream as I charged. "Kill 'em! Kill 'em! Kill 'em!" I stabbed it good then turned the rifle around and clubbed the shit out of the dummy until my rifle disintegrated into 40 pieces. With just the barrel left I continued to beat the metal pole that the dummy was fastened to it. The whole place erupted after that. The other guys were running around stabbing at dummies screaming their heads off and breaking rifles left and right. It was pandemonium and it was great! All the Sergeants loved it, but told us to tone it down a little coz we were breaking too many rifles.

★ ★ ★

One day, they took a bunch of us from the Company over to this building and told us that due to our test scores, we were qualified for Warrant Officer Training School to learn to fly helicopters. I thought that they must be dumb or desperate to pick me to fly a helicopter… I have no sense of direction. If I'm in 'Nam flying out to pick up some guys in the field, I'd end up in Japan, and they want me to fly? I was right about them being desperate though coz apparently a shit load of flyers were getting knocked out of the sky by Vietnamese armed with homemade rocket launchers and small arms fire. No way was I gonna be fodder for those crack shots. I'll take my chances on the ground. So I asked the officer in charge what would happen if I flunked out of the school (which regardless of whether I wanted to or not, I had a bad habit of doing).

"Oh not to worry," he says, "You'll just be put on gunner." Yah, a gunner. I could just see myself blasting away at some innocent farmer and his buffalo. Hell, I have a hard time killing a mouse! Luckily this school was voluntary, and I remembered what those old Vets told me, not to volunteer for anything, so I happily declined, and that was the end of my career as a helicopter pilot.

We graduated from Basic Training and got our orders for our next training school. I ended up going to a school and being trained to be something I always wanted to be besides a drummer and that was a heavy equipment operator. I loved it. The school was the best in the world and we got trained on a dozen machines from bulldozers to earthmovers. Then, two things happened at the same time that kept me out of 'Nam. The first was the 18th General Supply Company was being reactivated in Germany after being wiped out in a beach landing in Europe during WWII, and needed heavy equipment operators to run these giant forklifts that would load and unload trains and trucks. The second thing to happen was two guys at the 18th Supply headquarters were guitar pickers from Nashville who needed a drummer for their band. They found out about me and must have pulled some strings, because that's where I ended up. These two were waiting for me when I stepped off the train in Germany. I found out they were back up musicians in Nashville and I ended up playing with them off and on the entire time I was stationed there. We backed up all the Nashville singers that needed a band when they came to Europe and I got to meet a lot of those old time Nashville artists that way.

If you've ever seen "Mash" on TV, the 18th General Supply Company was 10 times crazier. I thought I was in a nut farm! I asked a guy in the office what the scoop was with all the nut cases and he said when they re-activated the Company, they asked Division to send down as many men as they could spare. Well, those First Sergeants weren't going to send the best of the best, they're gonna unload all the worst they got: Killers, drug dealers, rapists, alcoholics, and severe mental cases. At that time, the Army was a dumping ground for last chance felons and criminals and we had them all in the 18th. Being a troublemaker myself, I fit in perfectly with these guys. My first roommate, Baby Huey, was trying to get a "Section 8" like Clinger from Mash, so he'd do things like wear his uniform on backwards, his hat backwards and his boots on the wrong feet. He was always trying to get me to jump the fence and go AWOL, which he finally did and ended up joining a circus. One night, Me and Baby Huey were pulling guard duty when I first got to the company. We got a call that there was a race riot at the club on base and immediately Commander Cody lines us all up in a double formation. They start handing us out guns and we notice that the guns don't have any ammo in them! They must have been banking on the intimidation factor. I never did find out why they always gave us guns with no ammo, and if I learned anything in the Army it was "Don't Ask" coz you weren't going to get a straight answer anyways. So we start yelling to the Commander that we're not going over to stop a race riot with empty guns, and he says in response to this: "Forward March!" Baby Huey grabs me by the shirt and pulls me out of line and then pushes me back in line when the last guys pass us by. We're in quickstep and up ahead we can see about 200 guys tearing each other's heads off. Baby Huey grabs me again to slow me down and luckily it was dark so Commander Cody didn't see when we ducked behind a couple of trucks. "Forward men into the Malay!" He yelled gallantly, with his .45 held high in the air, his troops deciding that was a bad idea stayed back. All I can remember is a shirt flying in the air, then his .45, then a boot and that was it for Commander Cody. The rest of us hung around watching the action until a ton of MP's showed up and broke up the fun. I still wonder who got Commander Cody's .45.

When Baby Huey went AWOL and joined the circus, he was eventually caught and the Captain asked me if I would take him down to Headquarters so he could be sentenced. They issued me a .45 with no clip in it… here we go again, what did they expect me to do with an empty gun if he tried to escape? Point it at him and go, "BANG! BANG! You're dead!?" Despite, I agreed to go coz it got me off base for a little while anyways. Baby Huey was begging me to stop at this base on the way to Headquarters so he could visit with his buddy before he went to jail. It just so happened that one of my old buddies from Tangle Town, Dave Seablom, was stationed there, so I reluctantly caved in. I told him he had one hour to visit and then meet back at the jeep. The hour comes and goes, I say goodbye to Dave and go back to the jeep and wait for Huey. 15 minutes go by. No Huey. A half hour, no Huey. I knew at that point he had skipped. I checked all over the base for him and ask around but no one was talking. I return to base, sans Huey, and go before the Captain. "Baby Huey skipped on me sir." I said.

"And just how did he do that?" The Captain asks visibly pissed.

"Well, at one point he had to take a pee, so I took his cuffs off and he made me turn my back coz he was pee shy and when I turned back around he was running through the field we had stopped at. I took out the .45 and yelled 'BANG! BANG!' but I must have missed him coz he kept going. I chased him for a few miles but eventually lost him when he hopped a train."

"Good work," says the Captain, "Don't worry, we'll catch him again." The Captain was right. They caught him a month later and in the end, Huey finally got his wish and was washed out of the Army with a Dishonorable Discharge.

I was assigned to the motor pool where I had a forklift to maintain at the depot. Out of all our jeeps and trucks only one truck worked. Everything else was junk, and the Master Sergeant, Lucca Donnato, who was this big Italian guy with Mob connections, told us we needed to get the Company in tip top shape for inspection from Headquarters and he didn't care how we did it. Lucky for us we had a bunch of guys from New York City who were car thieves and worked in chop shops. They went around to other Army Bases and Motor Pools and stole all the parts we needed for our own. They even stole a truck so they had a vehicle to haul all the stolen parts they got!

Our Company was located on the second floor of this huge building in the city of Darmstadt. There were sleeping rooms and down the hall was the office and the mailroom. The guys from a different outfit stayed downstairs below us in one big 8-

man room. They would party all night long and keep the rest of us awake until the wee hours of the morning. One Saturday night they were being really loud, drinking, fighting, and arguing. Everyone in our room had to pull weekend shift and get up at 5 a.m. I went down there and told the Officer-on-Duty and he went and shut them up. Well not 5 minutes later they started up again, and this continued until we had to get up the next morning. I was fed up. Something had to be done to pay these guys back. I had bought these things called Block Busters off this German guy who had a shop across the street, which were like a quarter stick of TNT. To help with my little plan, I got a hold of this little guy called Dunn who was straight off a farm in Lower Michigan who I pulled out of a few scraps with the Section Chief, so he owed me one. Well, one Sunday morning, the guys downstairs were sleeping off their wild ass party from the night before. I told Dunn to go downstairs and hook 3 of the Block Busters through the window and run. We were at the second floor window giving him the high sign, when the Officer-of-the-Day walks into our room.

"NO! Dunn!" I yell out the window. "Forget about it!" But it was too late. KAPLOW! KAPLOW! KAPLOW! The three go off in succession. We hear screaming and yelling and I see a couple of guys diving out of the their window and tumble into the street. And I didn't even get to enjoy it. Two minutes later Dunn comes running into the room.

"How did I do Hoolie, how did I do?" Dunn asks.

"Oh just great Dunn, and I'd like you to meet the Officer of the Day who's going to arrest our asses now." Me and Dunn did two weeks of hell scrubbing pots and pans in the kitchen, but it was worth every minute. We were the heroes of our company.

I come from a long line of bullshitters so I never had a problem with the Officers of our company believing everything I said. They knew I was a musician and a pretty good cook and that my family owned and operated a bar, so they asked me to come to an Officer's party to serve drinks and grill steaks. The steaks were no problem, but I didn't know shit about mixed drinks. I didn't know a Martini from an Alexander, I just knew shots and beer. But nevertheless they gave me money to purchase the booze. I figured that most of the Officers were fresh out of college and ROTC and probably got loaded at a frat party at least once, and since I didn't know the first thing about making mixed drinks, I thought I'd do the next best thing: A Yooper Wop-a-Toolie. I got a huge 5-gallon mix bowl and I dumped in Orange Juice, Hawaiian Punch, a quart of Vodka, Beefeaters, Rum, and Canadian Club. It was a smash hit. Boy did those Officers get blasted on that Wop-a-Toolie, and so did their wives! And while the officers were off talking about playing soldier, all their sexy wives hung around me, telling me how creative I was and how much they hated Army life and all the while touching me non stop! It sure pays being a bullshitter sometimes!

But an even bigger bullshitter than me was Beaver, a Cuban guy that I hung out with that was from DC and worked in my section. He had all the guys believing that he was a black belt in Karate. So some big dumb shit would start giving him crap and Beaver would jump up and scream and do his Kung Fu moves and they would always get this dumb founded look on their faces and would back off. I laughed like a bugger at these bullies. They were so easy to bullshit. Beaver sang and played guitar and he and I would sit in his room and write songs and dream about going to Brazil and playing rock and roll. He'd tell me that I had to move to Brazil with him when we got out of the army, that we'd make a fortune. He was always trying his bullshit on me so I'd tell him:

"Listen man, don't waste your breath. You can't bullshit a bullshitter, eh."

"No I'm telling you the truth! My Dad was the Ambassador to Brazil under Johnson. I'm not lying to you!"

"Sure Beaver," I'd tell him, "Prove it." Sure enough, two weeks later, he gets a package which contained a picture of him, his mom, dad, and President Johnson. Boy, was I ever confused. When I got out of the service I was going to hook up with him out in DC and we were going to start a band. I was packed up and on my way when I stopped to gas up at the Spur Station in downtown Ishpeming. I hear a shout and it was a friend of mine who was heading for Milwaukee to look for work. He convinced me to go to Milwaukee with him instead, and well, the rest is history.

Another guy I hung around with was Shelly. He was a slick dressing southern boy from South Carolina and had to be in crime of some sort coz he looked and acted the part of one cool laid back dude, just like in the movies. He always carried a gun whenever we went out and all of the tough guys gave him ground and respected him. We were at a bar one time in Frankfort when this free for all broke out between the Army and Air Force. Everyone in the bar was throwing punches or being punched. Shelly slowly stands up and says to me: "I'm not getting my cloths dirty over nothing. Let's get out of here." Then he reaches into his inside pocket and pulls out his 38 snub nose and starts blasting into the ceiling. It was amazing to see all those guys clear a path for us all the way to the door. Shelly was the Burt Reynolds of the 18th General Supply Company.

In the end, I had a great time when I was overseas. Coming from Ishpeming, I wasn't exposed to many different colors and cultures. I was taught by my Mother not to be prejudiced, but it wasn't until I was serving, that I got to put that to the test. I met a lot of great guys and got along with all of them: Mexican, Puerto Rican, Blacks, Whites, Japanese, Chinese, Indian, and many others in between. They taught me that color is only skin deep, and by keeping an open mind and just being myself, they in turn accepted me as a friend.

Hoolie & Chief,
Two Upper Michigan natives

Hoolie and gang, basic training

Hoolie,
Heavy equipment advanced training

Hoolie & Bra, One yooper,
one troll in Europe

Da gang of crazies, Daffy, Gen. Patton,
Col. Dumpie, Sags, Weiner, Hoolie

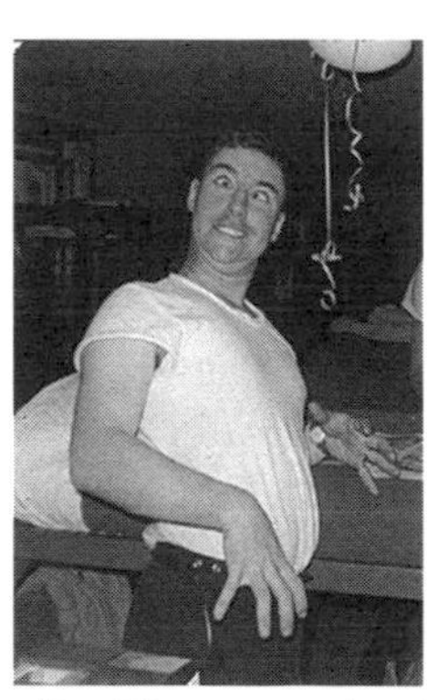

Hoolie, New years day 1967

A WALK ON THE BEACH

Brucksi Lynne was walking on South Beach along Lake Superior when he stumbled across an old lamp. He picked it up and rubbed the sand off of it, and lo and behold, a Yooper Genie pops out.

"Ok you got me out of dat bottle," says the genie, "Thanks, eh. I'm a Yooper genie so I can only grant you one wish."

Brucksi thought about it for awhile and said, "I've always wanted to go to Hawaii, but I'm too scared to fly and I get sick if I go on a boat. Could you build me a bridge to Hawaii so I can drive over there to visit?"

The genie laughs and said, "That's impossible!! Think of the logistics of that! How would the supports ever reach the bottom of the Pacific? Think of how much concrete, how much steel! No, think of something else, eh."

Brucksi was visibly disappointed but in the end said, "OK, I'll try and think of something real good," and then after a moment, "I've been married and divorced four times. My wives always said that I don't care and that I'm insensitive so, I wish that I could understand women, know how they feel inside and what they're thinking when they give me the silent treatment, know why they're crying, know what they really want when they say 'Nothing,' know how to make them truly happy."

The Yooper Genie replies, "Do you want that bridge to be two lanes or four?"

THE BEST NEW YEARS GIG EVER

WHEN I got out of the service back in '67, I was looking for a band to start up with playing drums. I searched and searched and finally hooked up with a buncha dudes from the Copper Country called "Lane Dawson and the Dawson Boys." What a group of crazy buggers they were. There was this one time at this New Years Eve gig—wait, hold on a sec, I'm getting ahead of myself. Before I get to that I should mention a few things about these guys.

Lane Dawson was a cross between Roy Orbison and young Marlon Brando. He had the whole nine yards: the dark glasses, jeans rolled up, a leather jacket and a motorcycle. The bass player was Dave Riutta, aka "Heikki Lunta," who was always disappearing before the gigs, presumably "to take a dump." When we'd finally find him, we could always tell what shape he was in by the number of drink sticks in his shirt pocket. He was nuts. Why is it that all bass players seem to be nuts? The years have taught me that if the bass player isn't nuts, they probably ain't worth a shit on the bass. Our steel guitar player was Weldon Mattson, from the planet Zurkonnanen. He was always trying to convince me that sleep was a waste of time, sometimes staying up for days and showing up at practice with these big purple bags under his eyes. This odd mix of personalities made for one helluva band. We'd all wear these red coats and black pants, and did a lot of good old country, some Buck Owens, some Polkas, and a lot of CCR. We played the UP/Wisconsin circuit of bars and dance halls and it was a blast. Hell, we even had people that would follow us around coz they liked us so much.

Alright, so like I was saying, it's New Years Eve 1968. Lane had booked us at a place called Snuffy's Saloon and the place was packed wall to wall with Jackpine Savages: Iron Range Hockey players, wild women, and an assortment of other crazies from around Marquette County. We started playing around 9:30. Since we weren't allowed to drink on stage, we had a sober vantage point (except maybe Dave) and we'd make a game out of checking out the crowd. I scanned the crowd and everyone looked like they were having a good time except for this old gummer who was sitting alone by the door. He apparently had been there celebrating all day, coz the table in front of him was full of empties and he was sitting there swaying back and forth and drooling. Right in the middle of this nice fast number, I take another scan of the crowd and notice Biker Niemi from the Iron Range Hockey Team (the bad asses of the Midwest) walking over to this woman sitting at a table next to the dance floor. She was sitting next to a skinny little guy who must've been her husband, and she shakes her head "no" to Biker who probably asked her to dance. About 15 minutes later Biker is back and again she refuses. He keeps this up 3 or 4 more times until finally the skinny husband jumps up and points his finger at Biker. Biker gives the guy a shove to the ground and goes back to hassling the woman. The skinny guy stands up, cocks his fist back and lets it fly. BAM! Right square on the side of Biker's head and down he goes, sprawled on the dance floor, out cold. Everyone kept dancing like nothing had happened, stepping all over him.

In the meantime, Biker's buddy, Big Nose Pusska another Iron Ranger, is wandering around the bar wondering where Biker went. After a few unsuccessful rounds of the bar, he finally spots him all sprawled out on the floor and goes over and picks him up. They almost get out the door when Big Nose stumbles and they both run into the drunken gummer that was passed out at the table next to the door. All the bottles and cans that were collected on the old man's table go flying, and the gummer jumps up and nails Big Nose right in the jaw. That's all it took. The one spark that ignited the fire, as they say.

The gummer and Big Nose fought their way back down the toward the dance floor, falling over tables and into booths, John Wayne style. The Old Man and Big Nose were like a tornado moving through the bar, the farther they moved into the bar, the more "stuff" or, in this case, people they picked up. By the time those two reached the dance floor, there had to be at least 30 people swinging at each other and more joining in every second: women screaming, bottles flying, old ladies hitting people with their purses, man it was great! We just kept on playing, trying to add background and timing to the punching, and when the "Tornado" reached the stage, the whole bar was in complete pandemonium.

All of a sudden Lane stops playing and points over by our P.A. speaker. We could see the speaker being slowly sucked into the chaos, the cord stretched out like a toe chain. Me and him dive into the crowd and follow the cord to the speaker and then crawled back to the stage, speaker in tow, without so much as a punch landing on us. Right when we get back on stage, we hear someone scream: "GET THE GUYS IN THE RED COATS!" We knew our safe time was up, so we backed up by my drums and took a running nosedive into the heart of the action. While all this is going on, Snuffy, the owner, who was only 5'2" but tougher than rawhide, was playing the edge of the fight with his bartender Big Eddy who was easily 400 lbs. As soon as some guy would come near the edge where Snuffy was, he'd cold cock them and toss him to Big Eddy who was by the back door. From there he'd toss them out back where they'd have to face Snuffy's dog Uncle Remis. Uncle

Remis was a recent graduate of attack dog school (top of the class) and a flunky of obedience school (for his unwavering tendency to eat people).

After the dive off the stage, I crawled my way over to the woman's john, hoping to find safe sanctuary, when all of a sudden some guy grabs me and without thinking, I let him have it in the gut. He went sailing backwards and knocked the john door right off the hinges. I looked back to the stage and saw that the rest of the band had made it back to the stage, and I yelled to them to start packing the stuff. No sooner had I finished saying this, than an old lady jumped on my back and wrapped her purse strap around my neck, closing off my wind. The more I spun around to get her off, the more she'd choke me. She kept yelling, "YOU STOMPED MY SON, YOU STOMPED MY SON!" I managed to back up toward a wall and proceeded to ram her into it 3 or 4 times until she slid off my back. After checking to see if she was out cold, I dragged her to Snuffy who tossed her to Big Eddy who in turn tossed her out the door to Uncle Remis.

Afterwards, the place was totally trashed. It was 11 o'clock and Snuffy paid us a full night and we beat it for Ishpeming to the Venice Bar to have a pizza and some drinks. We walked in just as people were raising their drinks and toasting to the New Year. It was the perfect ending to such a strange and chaotic night...

Uncle Bruno, Hoolie, Johnny Van
Jamming at The Royal 1967

Ernie Brown, Wild Bill. Morcom
Hoolie 1964

Left: 1965
The Penetrations
Hoolie, Dean Van,
Wild Bill, Jim Meyskens

Right:
Hoolie & Norm
1967 (the poor
woman that's put
up with me for all
these years

Below:
Da Yoopers 2005
Jim Bellmore,
Lynn Anderson, Hoolie,
Billy Langson, Reggie Lusardi, Bob Symons, Dick-e-Bird Bunce

MIRROR, MIRROR ON THE WALL

After living deep in the woods of the Upper Peninsula all his life, Gorman decided it was time to visit the big city of Marquette for the first time. While in town, he stops in at Wally World up on US-41, and after walking around the store in wide-eyed amazement, he picks up a mirror from a display and looks in it. Not knowing what it was, he says: "How about that, eh! Here's a picture of my daddy!" He bought the "picture," but on the way home he remembered his wife Olga didn't like his father. So he hung it in the shed and every morning before leaving for the woods, he would go out and look into the mirror.

Olga began to get suspicious of these morning trips to the woodshed. One day, after her husband left, she searched the barn and found the mirror, and as she looked into the glass, she fumed, "So that's the old bitch he's running after!"

SUNDAY DRIVE

Ski Binders Champion and his wife were out driving one day when a state cop pulled him over.

"What seems to be the problem, dere, eh?" Ski Binders asked.

The cop replied, "Sir, didn't you notice that your wife fell out of the car back there?"

"Oh thank God you told me that, for awhile there I thought I went deaf!"

THE ROYAL

MY GRANDMOTHER bought a small corner building in Downtown Ishpeming and turned it into the Royal Bar. The Bar eventually ended up in my Uncle Bruno's name and his three brothers bar tended. They were all great storytellers and funny guys. Everyone in town loved going in there coz it was non-stop entertainment. On Saturday nights, they would put comedy shows on and entertained folks for many years with their slapstick. When I was fourteen, I worked behind the bar and helped clean up on weekends, my first paying job. Uncle Bruno was like a second father to me and my mentor. I wanted to be just like him and make people laugh.

One day he was having his usual argument with one of the regulars, Sticky Niemi. They were arguing about who was the cheapest between the two of them. I got so tired of listening to this same argument day in and day out, so I decided to end it once and for all. I gave them both a dime each and told them to go out and see how far they could stretch it. Then come the following week, I would judge who was the cheapest. They both agreed and by next week I forgot all about the deal I made with them until they started up again on the same subject. I went over to the two of them to ask how they both spent their dime.

"So Uncle Bruno, what did you do with your dime?" I asked.

"Well, I went to Olsen's Newsstand and bought a ten cent cigar. The first day I smoked a third of it and saved the ashes, and on the second day I smoked another third of it and saved the ashes, and on the 3rd day I finished it and saved the ashes. On the fourth day I fertilized Aunty Penny's house plants with the ashes."

"Geez, that's really stretching a dime," I said a bit amazed by the answer. I could see old Sticky was twitching by now; he couldn't wait to tell me what he did with his dime.

"All right Sticky, what'd you do with your dime?" Sticky took a deep breath.

"I went to Rock's Meat Market and bought a bratwurst for ten cents. I took it home and peeled the skin off, fried it up and ate a third of the brat. On the second day, I ate another third, and on the third day I ate the rest of it. On the fourth day, I took the skin that I'd peeled off of it, and rinsed it out and used it that night for a condom. Then the fifth day I took a poop in that skin, and tied it back up, and I took it back to Rock's Meat Market. I told Old Man Rock that this bratwurst smells like shit. Old Man Rock gave it a sniff and said 'Yah you're right' and gave me my dime back, putting the bratwurst back into the case. So anyway, here it is." Sticky said slapping the dime down onto the bar with a huge grin on his face. With much grumbling from Uncle Bruno, I gave Sticky the title of "Cheapest Man in Ishpeming," a title that today is still unbroken.

I heard a couple days later that Old Man Rock sold that bratwurst to some Finlander as pepperoni.

"SHE BROKE MY GUTS!"

I WAS working at the Royal Bar one Saturday night and the place was packed. I worked one end, Bruno worked the middle, and Uncle Franky worked the other end. Shirley and Roy were regulars and they got into their usual Saturday night battle. Shirley was a big woman and could beat the crap out of any man who gave her shit. Roy was a skinny ninety-six pound beanpole of a guy. Finally, it got so bad, we had to toss them out before they destroyed the place. After getting tossed out, they went staggering into the Coffee Cup Restaurant down the street. Shirley told Roy not to let her order anything fattening coz she was on a diet. So when they placed their order, Roy ordered a large pizza with double cheese for himself and an order of dry toast for Shirley. That pissed Shirley off real good.

Roy spotted some friends across the restaurant and went over to bullshit a little with them. When the food came and Roy was still bullshitting, Shirley couldn't resist taking a piece of Roy's pizza. Just as she was sliding a piece down her yahzoo, Roy came back and caught her. Before Roy even opened his mouth to yell at her, she took a swing at him and as he was ducking, she grabbed the plate of dry toast and nailed him on the top of the head with it. He grabbed the pizza and smashed her on the top of the head with it, and took off running for the Royal.

In they came, him facing her, walking backwards, and her screaming like hell. She looked like the Creature from the Black Lagoon with mozzarella cheese and cudhigi hanging down to her shoulders moving like a bull mouse in heat. Bruno who was the closest, and a squat man of 5'2", jumped off the bar and onto Shirley's back. She had Bruno on her back like a sack of potatoes, spinning round and round and hitting everyone in sight. She ended up slipping on a puddle of beer and landing square on her back, flattening Bruno to a pancake in the process.

"GET HER OFF ME, SHE BROKE MY GUT! I CAN FEEL IT! MY GUT JUICE IS EVERYWHERE!" He kept yelling and yelling. We managed to roll her off poor Bruno. He got up and took a look at himself and then smelled his hands. "Oh hell, she didn't break my gut, she just peed all over me. I gotta go upstairs and change." When Bruno got upstairs to the apartment he and my Aunt Penny shared, she started in on him, slapping him non-stop.

"What the hell is going on downstairs? You fooling around with those women again? Look at you, you no good for nothing. Why the hell do you smell like pee? Nag, nag, nag... ."

Poor uncle Bruno got the hell beat out of him twice. Some nights it seems, you just can't win.

WING NUTS

I WAS cleaning up the bar one Saturday, when these two Wing Nuts came in from the local air base.

Uncle Bruno was there with me and he asked them, "Whaddaya want?"

"Some beer," one of them replied.

"I gotta see some ID," said Bruno.

"You don't need to see our ID's, we're from the Base you old fart," the tall one said.

"I got a better idea, how about you get out," Bruno told them with a stiff glare.

"Can't we at least have a Coke?" the tall one pleaded. Reluctantly, he poured them two Cokes, and the short one picked up the cokes and poured them on the bar.

"Get the hell out!" Uncle Bruno yelled.

"I'm sorry, it won't happen again, can we just have two more cokes? I swear it was an accident." the tall one asked innocently. Bruno again filled up two more Cokes, but was obviously irritated. The tall one grabbed them this time and dumped them out onto the bar.

"ALL RIGHT, GET THE HELL OUT OF HERE AND DON'T COME BACK!" Bruno screamed at them. They sauntered out the door laughing the whole way, and not five minutes later were back, this time with a friend who had to be at least 6'5".

"Three beers," the spokesman for the three piped up.

"Are you guys nuts? Get the hell out of my bar!" Bruno stood his ground. Surprisingly too, seeing as he tops 5'2" with thick soled shoes. The big friend grabbed Bruno and dragged him over the bar.

"Give us three beers or die!" The big guy yelled in his face.

"O.k, o.k, I'll get them," Bruno replied in a meek voice. When the big guy let him down, Bruno continued, "I have to go downstairs to get the beer coz there's none left here in the cooler. Don't worry, they'll be nice and cold."

"That's better old man," the tall spokesman said, "And hurry up, coz we're thirsty." Little did they know that Bruno kept his Spanish-American War rifle with a four-foot bayonet in the basement. The next thing these guys see is this pug of a man running up from the basement with a rifle in his hands yelling:

"I'M GONNA STICK YOU LIKE THE PIGS YOU ARE! AH, AH, AH, AH!!"

They flew out the door with Uncle Bruno right on their ass. He stuck the big guy right in the bum as he rounded the corner. Bruno was still not back a half hour later, and I was just about to go out and start looking for him when the cops came in the back door of the Royal. "Is Bruno here?" One of them asks.

Like a good nephew I reply, "No he's out at the Carp River fishing."

"Oh, well, we have reports of a little short guy with a cigar in his mouth and a six foot gun chasing three guys all over town. Are you sure he's not here?"

"No, he left early this morning and said he wouldn't be back until late."

"Oh, o.k. well, you tell him when he gets back that we were here to see him," the cop said with that unbelieving tone to his voice.

"Will do." I said as they filed out the same door they came in.

GOOD OLD JUMBO

THE ROYAL Bar was a hang out for the miners in Ishpeming. When work let out at 3:30, the bar would fill up with hard drinking miners trying to wash down some of the dust they swallowed during the day. By 4 o'clock, it was three thick at the bar. During the day before this rush, though all we had in there was the usual barflies that were always hanging around. Jumbo Freeberg was one of the guys that was always there, always sitting in the same seat. He'd start early in the morning and then take a nap at the bar around two and then wake up for the rush at four where he knew he could mooch some drinks off some the miners he knew.

One day, about an hour before the rush, my uncle Bruno told me to wake up Jumbo. I went to shake him, and he didn't move. Stiffer than a doornail. Uncle Bruno checked him out and told me to call Dr. Bertucci who had an office next door. Doc came in and checked him out and pronounced him dead. "I'll go call Fassbender's Funeral Home to come pick him up," Doc said solemnly.

In the meantime, guys started piling into the bar for afternoon rush. They all gathered around Jumbo and were slapping him on the back and Herby Ruspuckka was yelling in his ear, "Come on Jumbo, wake up and have a drink on Old Herby, you old goat!" This went on for about an hour. Guys were buying Jumbo drinks and slapping him on the back. There was even a guy carrying on a conversation with him about planting gardens and cow shit. Jumbo had at least twelve shots of booze in front of him when the door swung open and in come the two undertakers from Fassbenders Funeral Home with the stretcher. The place went dead silent. They came over and lifted Jumbo onto the stretcher and wheeled him out the door.

The minute the door shut, the place went right back to its noisy hum. The guys that were sitting by Jumbo grabbed up the shots that were still untouched and said, "Well, can't let these go to waste. Here's to old Jumbo!" as they tipped the bottoms of the glass skyward.

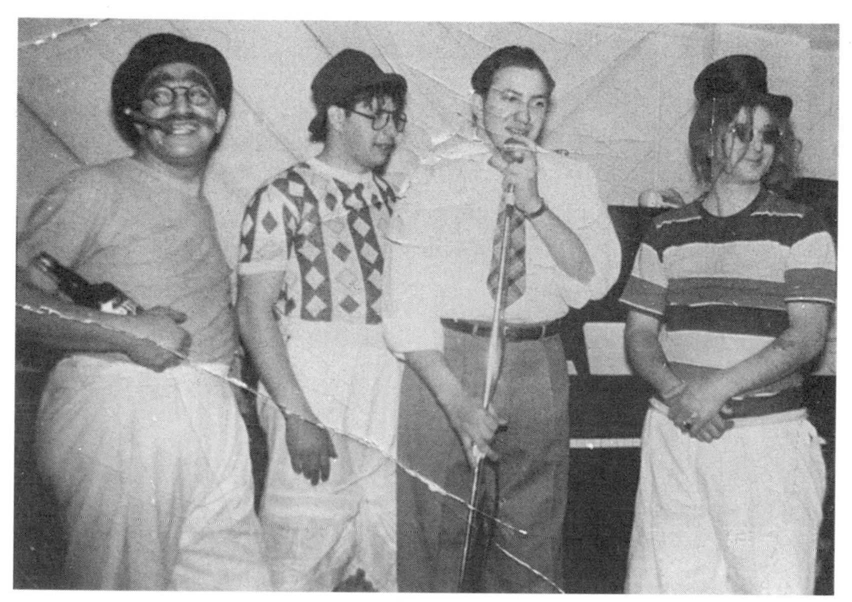

Da Royal Bar Gang:
My uncles Joe, Tudy, Frankie Sarvello and Angelo Portale

My uncle Joe Sarvello doing his Groucho Marx routine

BACKSEAT HUNTER

A carload of Yoopers was Downstate looking for a place to hunt. They found a farm just off of I-75 and pulled into the yard. Rudy went up to the house to ask the farmer permission to hunt on his land. The farmer was agreeable.

"Sure you can hunt here, but would you do me a favor? That old mule standing over there is 20 years old and sick with cancer, but I don't have the heart to kill her. Would you do it for me?"

Feeling obligated to the nice farmer, Rudy said, "Sure I will," and headed back to the car for his gun. While en route, he decides to play a trick on his hunting buddies. He got into the car and when they asked if the Farmer said OK, he said, "He says we can't hunt here but I'm gonna teach that old coot a lesson." With that he rolled down his window, stuck his gun out and blasted the mule. "There that will teach him!"

And just as he said that a second shot rang out from the backseat and Roy, his hunting buddy exclaimed, "I got the Cow!"

SO YOU WANNA KNOW WHERE THE DEER ARE AT TOO?

UNCLE BRUNO was what you'd call an all-round sportsman. He was a steady hunter of rabbits, birds and deer, along with being an avid fisherman, so he really fit in with this crowd. He could go on for hours telling stories about his misadventures in the woods, which is what he was doing when I walked in on this particular afternoon. It was two in the afternoon during hunting season, and the Royal Bar was packed. Bruno and Frankie were working the bar. I was playing with Johnny and the Playboys at the Diamond Club that night, and had stopped at the Royal for a while before going to the club. There was the usual pack of local regulars, most of them dressed in their hunting clothes along with a mix of Downstate hunters laughing and having a good time.

I had been there not ten minutes when these four hunters from Detroit walked in and sat right next to me at the bar. After they ordered a round from Bruno they asked him where the deer are. A fatal mistake. All the regulars in the bar who heard that got real quiet, cause they knew what was coming.

Bruno says: "Deer? You wanna know where da deer are at too?"

"Yeah," says one of the hunters. "We heard you were the expert on deer hunting and could tell us where to go. You're Bruno, ain't you?"

"Uh-huh," Bruno replies, and by this time we all know what he's cooking up in that brain of his, and after a pause he continues:

"I know a spot where a huge buck's been spotted all week and no one I know has claimed it yet. I already got my buck; otherwise I'd be there right now. Now, not too many people know about this spot, so don't go telling no one. Just go down Division Street two blocks, turn left, and then go two miles until you get to Millimaki's Gas Station. It's closed now, so don't worry, they don't care if you hunt dere. Just park your car across the road and wait. Right dere is where that big buck has been spotted crossing da road."

Well, I could see the gleam in those Apple Knockers eyes as they drank up and headed for the door. Right as they walked outside, all the regulars in the bar ran to the windows to watch those guys ramble on down Division Street and make the turn on Pine to go to Millimaki's Station.

When their truck was out of sight, the bar erupted in hoots, howls, and laughter. Classic Bruno. What a perfect set up. Little did these guys know that Bruno had sent them to not only one of the busiest roads in Marquette County, but a spot that leads out to south country where The Wayside Bar is, and where a hell of a lot of guys hunted and drank. The only thing was that the deer hunting area was another twelve miles down the road, and these guys were still in the suburbs of Ishpeming where tons of cars and pickups would pass by them and laugh at the idiots hunting where no one in there right mind would hunt.

About an hour later, to everyone's surprise, in walks those same hunters Bruno had just sent out. They sit down at the bar and Bruno walks over to them. "You boys done hunting already?" He says with a snicker. One of the guys swells up with pride and says,

"Yes, we're done for the day."

"Hell man," Bruno replies, "don't get discouraged so easily, you gotta stay out there at least a couple of hours, anyway."

"Oh no," one of the hunters pipes up with excitement, "we didn't have to. No sooner did we find the place and get our guns out of the cases when this huge twelve-point buck walks across the road, right where you said he would. Well I aimed and BAM! One shot and down he went. Do you know anyone who could gut it for us?"

Bruno at this point was dumbfounded. He runs over to the window and takes a look at one of the biggest bucks he ever saw, strapped to the Apple Knocker's front fender. "Holy shit!" Bruno gasps. "What a monster! You got him by Millimaki's Gas Station?"

"Yeah, right where you said," the hunter said with a huge grin.

"Holy Shit I'm heading out dere to Millimaki's Gas Station!"

And out the back door he goes, rifle in hand. Everyone in the bar started laughing like hell, at the vision of cars whizzing by laughing at the short Italian guy standing on the side of road, hunting where no one in their right mind would hunt.

STEALING RAY

Ray and Rudy were buddies who went hunting every year for thirty years and never got a deer. One evening during deer season, Rudy came back to the camp dragging a beautiful 10-point buck. Grandpa was out getting wood for the stove when he spots Rudy dragging the buck. "Where's Ray?" Gramps asks.

"Ray's back dere three miles or so. He's laying in a snow bank alongside the trail. I think he had a coronary or something. He shot the deer then he grabbed his chest and spun around a couple of times." Rudy says.

"You left your best friend laying in a snow bank and you dragged this buck all the way back to the camp?" Gramps said astonished.

"I'll tell you something Gramps it was the hardest decision I had to make in my life. But then I thought, who the hell's gonna steal Ray anyways?"

IQ, Do You?

Spags Aho and his young son went out south to rabbit hunt with the family Beagle. After about an hour they finally came across some rabbit tracks. In between the track, there were little brown pellets, and Spag's son said to him: "Dad, what are those?"

Spags replied, "Those are smart pills. Try a couple, they'll make you smarter." So the kid grabbed a couple and put them in his mouth. He scrunched up his face and spit them out.

"Ewww! Yuk! They taste like poop!" The son said scooping up some snow and jamming it into his mouth.

"See, your getting smarter already!" Spags said, laughing.

WHY I NEVER HUNT DEER

IT WAS opening day of deer season 1964. I drove out north of Ishpeming where I had my blind built on the edge of a giant cedar swamp. No sooner did I sit down in the blind than the biggest buck I ever saw came waltzing in about 30 yards away from me! So, I slowly took aim and... click. What the hell?!! The buck looks at me briefly and goes back to eating on the bait pile. I take aim again and... click. Nothing. I started examining my gun, when I notice the buck walking towards me. Sweating shaking and fumbling, I raise the gun once more and... click. Just then I realized what the problem was... I forgot to load the gun! I was steaming mad, I grabbed my rifle by the barrel and ran out screaming, hoping I might get him across the forehead with it. Just as my rifle was whizzing towards his head, he ducks and I shatter the stock on a tree that was just on the other side of his head. The buck looks at me, shakes his head and jogs off toward the swamp. "Oh no you don't," I said and took off after him, flying like the wind. The chase kept up steady for 3 or 4 miles through swamp and hills, the buck running just fast enough for me to keep up. Pretty soon, I started huffing and puffing and stumbling on my ass. Completely out of breath, I finally collapsed against a tree. Who did I think I was? Hawkeye? There was no way I was going to stay with this buck. So I started hoofing it back to the truck, back through the swamp, over a big maple ridge, through a huge field and into another cedar swamp. Coming into this second swamp, I started realizing that nothing looked familiar, and that maybe I was lost. So disregarding everything I learned in Boy Scouts, I panicked and took off running in any old direction I could. In my disorientation, I was getting tangled in tag elders, slamming into trees, tripping on roots and at one point I fell into an ice cold creek up to my neck…

The cold water sobered me up a little to take stock of my situation. I figured that first I had to get out of my wet cloths, so I took them off and hung them in a tree, and dug in the pockets for matches to build a fire. That plan was soon extinguished when I found my only matches in the front pocket of my wet overalls completely soaked through. I stood there freezing in my long johns, shivering like mad with my lips turning blue. Now I really needed to get back to the truck. So I grabbed what was left of my rifle and struck out in a random direction. I didn't make it more than a few feet when I jumped over a big old cedar log and on top of a brush pile that had a big nasty bear sleeping under it! Up jumps that nasty bugger growling and showing his razor teeth. It didn't take much to get my feet moving the hell out of there. He took off after me like I was his first meal he'd seen in months. It felt like 3 hours went by and that bear was still chasing me, and at one point he was about to take a bite out of my ass, when my saving grace came up ahead. Sitting on a stump eating a pasty and crying was a "Troll" hunter from Downstate who was lost as well. That bear must have gotten a whiff of that pasty because the next time I looked back, the bear was tearing off after the "Troll." Relieved, I stood there shivering and starving. I checked around the stump to see if that Apple Knocker dropped any crumbs of pasty, but all I ended up finding was a stump full of frozen mushrooms… the kind we always picked in the fall. I figured that since they were frozen that they must still be good, and at that point I was past the point of caring, so I woofed them down in a matter of seconds. It didn't take but five minutes for my stomach to start turning like a washing machine and the hallucinations to start. By some dumb luck, after wandering around in a psychedelic stupor for another hour, I stumbled onto the main road, about 1 mile from where I had parked the truck. When I finally got back to the truck I couldn't believe my eyes... there was that old swamp buck eating the apples out of the bed of the truck. He took one look at me in my disheveled state and let out this sound that I swear was a laugh! I couldn't take it anymore. I hauled back and threw my rifle as hard as I could at him and it missed and smashed out the taillight. I ran to the truck hoping to get in and run the bugger over, but when I felt for my keys I realized they were in my hunting pants hanging on that tree back in the woods. I snapped. I took my rifle and started beating the hell out of my truck...

When I got out of Bell Hospital a week later, I cut my deer license into million pieces and sent it back to the DNR along with the hospital bill for frostbite and food poisoning. This is why I don't go deer hunting anymore.

911, HOW CAN I HELP YOU?

A couple of hunters from Detroit are out hunting deer north of Ishpeming when one of them falls to the ground. His friend runs over to him and found that his eyes were rolled in the back of his head and he didn't appear to be breathing. Without thinking, he whips out his cell phone and calls 911.

Shirley Maki, the operator answers and he gasps: "I think my friend is dead! What can I do?" Shirley, in a calm, soothing, Yooper voice says, "Just take it easy dere chum. I can help yah. First. Let's make sure the bugger's dead, eh!" There was a silence and then she hears a gunshot go off through the phone. After awhile the Mittenhead comes back on the line. "Ok, now what?"

WHERE'S THE BEEF?

Pinky Anderson kills a deer and brings it home. He decides to clean it and serve the venison for supper. He knows his kids are fussy eaters and won't eat it if they know what it is, so he decides not to tell them. His little boy keeps asking him, "What's for supper, Dad?" And Pinky tells him each time:

"You'll see! Just hold your horses!" Suppertime rolls around, and the venison is served. To his joy, Pinky sees his kids eating the venison, but the daughter is relentless. "Dad, what are we eating?" Until Pinky can't take it anymore.

"Ok, ok, I'll give you a hint," he says still weary about telling them, "It's what your mother sometimes calls me."

The daughter spits the meat out and screams, "We're eating asshole??!!

BIRD HUNTING

DAVE CAME up with the bright idea of stealing his old man's 52 Chevy so we could go cruising the back roads for birds. His old man was midnight shift so we had plenty of time to hunt, coz he'd sleep until 6 pm. We pushed the car out of the garage, and down the road until we got far enough away from the house to start it up. Vito and Dave were in the front seat and me and Joey were in the back seat. Joey was a nervous twitch ass that was always worried about everything, like in this case getting caught with Dave's old man's car. He had his shotgun loaded and pointed at the ceiling and he was tapping on the trigger nervously. Dave, in his usual stock car racer mode was wheeling down the dirt roads, flying through puddles and over big ruts. We were laughing and screaming when all of a sudden, Dave nails a big swamp hole and— BAM! Joey's gun goes off. He shot the ceiling all to hell: the cloth was hanging down over Joey's head and there was about 2000 BB holes peppering the roof, not to mention the car was filled with gun smoke. We pull the car over and got out. We couldn't stop laughing... everyone except Joey who was crying.

"Holy shit!" Vito yells, "take a look at the roof!" All the paint was gone where the blast had hit and it looked like the car had 2000 little pimples all over it. After our fit of laughter stopped, reality set in. We needed a quick fix it. So we headed over to Eddie's house and got his old man's hammer and started pounding the hell out of the roof trying to take the pimples out. Then we got some black paint and rolled it onto the roof. Joey's in the inside with me trying to sew the cloth back up with fishing line. After we got everything done, we look her over and figure that Dave's old man will never notice coz he's so short and can't see the roof anyway. About 100 yards from Dave's house, we stop the car again and start pushing it up the driveway. Just as we pass close to the house, we hear Dave's old man shouting from above us:

"What the hell happened to my car?" We look up and there he is standing on the 2nd floor outside deck looking directly down at the roof of the car. We told him that some guys stole his car and shot the hell out of it with a shot gun and luckily we stumbled onto it abandoned in the woods and pushed it home because Dave wasn't allowed to drive it. It was pretty good story, but in the end, the old man didn't buy it. Man, did Dave catch hell for that one.

COME ON TAKE A RIDE

VITO IS my best chum. . . like a brother and a best buddy rolled into one. Vito was the kind of guy that always got me into some kind of shit one way or another. I knew that when I hung out with him, it's only a matter of time until something crazy happens. Like the time I was sitting patiently at my house waiting for the Packers and the Bears game to start one Sunday afternoon awhile back. It was a big play-off game and I didn't want to miss it for anything. Vito's psychic radar must've went off, which incidentally only goes off when I simply want to stay home and vegetate, coz not long after I sunk into my Lazy Boy, he's knocking on my door.

"Hey Hoolie, come take a ride with me to the camp, I gotta pick up some spare tires," he says.

"No, no, I can't, there's a big game coming on and I don't want to miss it, I know how it is when I go somewhere with you, something always happens."

"Aw come on, it'll only take 30 minutes tops, out and back and that's it."

"Bullshit, it's never 'out and back and that's it,'" I says back, "some kind of shit's always happening, I'm staying here where I'm safe."

"Hoolie, come on, I PROMISE I'll have you back in a flash... come on, come on... come..."

"All right!" I scream. "But, out and back and that's it. No stoppin' and screwing around. I don't wanna miss this game." I head out after him, deciding to just go as I was: T-shirt, jeans, and bedroom slippers.

"Oh yeah,"Vito says over his shoulder as he reaches the car, "Grab your gun in case we see a bird."

At this point I don't argue, I just comply and grab the 410 out of the garage and off we go. We get to the camp and Vito loads up the tires into his trunk. "Lets take a look up in the field across from the pond over there," he says.

"No way, I only got my bedroom slippers on and I ain't walking nowhere, besides I want to get back for the game... 'out and back' remember?" I reply.

"Aaah! We got plenty a time, come on," he says, "just 5 minutes, there's a nice path to walk on, and who knows maybe we'll scare up a bird or two." I reluctantly follow him (what else was I gonna do?) and we start into the field. After about 10 minutes of walking and no "nice path" to be found, I stop and yell to Vito who's by this time several yards ahead of me:

"Hey, come on, let's go back, my feet hurt in these bedroom slippers and I'm probably missing the kick off, and by the way, where the hell is this 'nice path' you're talking about?"

"I think it's back that way," he says and points back to where we came from. "Follow me." We walk and walk and walk. Suddenly the terrain starts to look really unfamiliar. I stop again.

"O.k. Hawk Eye, where the hell is this path?" I say, irritation bubbling in my voice.

"Uuuuhhhmmm, I think over here," and with that Vito strikes the old "Pathfinder" pose, putting his hand over his eyeballs and scanning the terrain.

"Uh-oh," I think. "Vito are we lost? If we are, don't say nothing, just climb that pine tree over there and see if you can see the camp from here or I'm gonna shoot your ass with this 410." He saw the flames in my eyes. He raced up the tree in no time.

"Well I can see the basin over there, so I think the camp is somewhere over there," as he points in an arbitrary direction and then shimmies back down the tree.

"Come on, I know a short cut from here, where we can get to the camp in five minutes. Yeah, I know where we are now."

"Yeah," I say, "Lost." We start walking his "short cut" and five minutes later something starts happening to the ground.

"Vito, I think we're sinking."

"Naaa, you're just—-" Before he could finish, we plunged straight into a swamp and within seconds were up to our armpits in muck, all scratched to shit and getting bit by 5 lb. bloodsucking mosquitoes. I really wanted to kill Vito at that point. We finally crawled out the other side of the swamp and we both collapse on the side of a maple ridge.

"Vito, I'm gonna kill you now." I said calmly between breaths.

"Uhh, yeah, how about I carry that 410 for yuh for awhile," he says with a big shit-eating grin on his face.

"No, then I won't have anything to kill you with." We finally catch our breath and start walking again. About a half hour later we make it out to a dirt road. My arms, face and hands were swollen from bugs chewing on me and my feet are swollen coz I got on goddamn bedroom slippers, not to mention the fact that the game was started by now and we don't know where the hell we are. We decided to toss a coin as to what direction to go and it came up "heads" so we went left.

After another twenty minutes of walking, we came out on a familiar site: North Camp Road. We finally knew where we were: seven miles away from Vito's camp. Just as I was about to raise the gun to bash Vito, we heard laughing coming from the woods on the other side of the road. We followed it and came to a clearing where a bunch of teenagers were sitting on their car drinking beer. I walked in the clearing with the 410 in tow and Vito following behind, and said:

"All right kids, if you don't give us a ride back to our camp, I'm gonna drop you right here and now."

We must not have been very threatening, full of swamp muck and mosquito bites and me with my bedroom slippers, coz all they did was burst out laughing at us. Me and Vito looked at one and another and realized we did look a tad bit pathetic... we couldn't help but laugh also. They good-naturedly gave us a ride back to Vito's camp and I made Vito give them the rest of the beer he had in the refrigerator.

I got home in time for the second half of the game. After the game I limped over to Vito's (my feet were so bad that I could barely walk) to kill him. When I got there, he talked me into taking a ride with him out to Skandia to pick up an old double barrel shot gun that some farmer was selling.

"It'll only take an hour," he says.

"O.k. but no stopping and screwing around this time."

"No screwing around, down and back, one hour, tops," he replied with a grin.

"O.k., down and back, one hour...I gotta be back in time for Benny Hill." And with that we hobbled into his car and drove off just as the sun was tipping below the pines.

FISHING WITH VITO

VITO IS a pilot so he gets to check out all the good fishing spots while flying. One time after he got back from flying, he told me that he found what looked like the headwaters of the Clark Creek out north of Ishpeming. The Clark was an ice cold creek with tons of trout in it. Vito suggested that we go and look for those headwaters, and that sounded like a good plan to me.

He picked up me and Eddy Villeneuve in his '56 Chevy and headed out north, crossing the Clark into some real wild country. We came within a 1/2 mile of the pond when we ran into a swampy area with a 3 foot by 20 foot long mud hole.

"Don't even try to go through there, let's park here and walk the rest of the way," I says.

"No the heck with that... why walk when we can drive... we'll make it," Vito replied.

"All right," I said reluctantly, seeing no use in arguing with Vito coz we were going to do it anyway. "I'll get out and guide you." Me and Eddy got out of the car and I say, surveying the area ahead: "If you keep you left wheels in the center hump and the other two wheels on the right edge, you might make it, but GO SLOW." Vito backs up the Chevy around the bend in the road until he's out of sight. "Hey! What the hell are yuh doin?" I yell. I could hear him winding up the Chevy's motor. Oh no, I knew it. Here he comes around the corner, pedal to the boards and "fish tailing" it! He misses the mud hole completely and goes airborne straight off the road and down into the swamp.

"ARE YOU NUTS?" I yell down to him, the car slowly sinking in the swamp. "Shit. Now we're going to have to dig you out and put something under the tires for traction. You got a shovel and a jack, right Vito?"

Vito replies, "Uuuhhhhmmm, well here's the thing. You know how bad the trunk was rusted out, right? Well one night the sucker finally caved in, and you know, since I didn't have a spare anyway, I figured why have a jack, right? And the shovel, well, what the hell do I need a shovel for anyway?"

I didn't say anything and simply pointed to the road in the direction we came from. Without a word Vito turned and started hoofing it back the 10 miles to town. Me and Eddy sat and waited, eating Ritz crackers that I had brought with me.

About a half hour later, We see a truck with three people in it, one of them being Vito with a huge toothy grin on his face. The lucky bugger must of ran into the only two people that had been out this way in the last 3 weeks. After a lot of shoveling and jacking, we managed to pull the Chevy out by night fall and we headed back to town without even getting a line wet.

Me and Eddy thought about killing Vito, but before we could he talked us into doing some night fishing at this pond he spotted up by Michigamme while flying...he told us he found what looked like the headwaters of the Tioga River.

Two real crazy guys! Left: Uncle Bruno & Aunty Penny.
Right: Old man Dahl with Rebel Da Wonder Dog.

Lume-a-toolie, Ron Ivey, Hoolie,
Buckie Dahl

Lume, Leon-burger, Buckie

Hoolie, Buckie, Lume, Ron

Lume, Hoolie,
Guges & Rob Seablom

EMPLOYEE OF THE MONTH

Because jobs are scarce here in the U.P., sometimes us Yoopers have to move away from our beloved home and find opportunity in bigger cities. Well, this one bright Yooper lad went to Detroit where he applied for a salesman job at one of the biggest department stores in Michigan.

"Have you ever been a salesman before?" The Head Guy asked him during his interview.

"Yes I was a salesman up in the U.P.," the Yooper lad answered confidently. The Boss took to the young lad immediately and told him he could start the next day.

"I'll check and see how you're doing at the end of the day tomorrow." The Boss said patting him on the back.

The next day was long and hard and at 5 o' clock when the doors were being locked for the day, the boss found the Yooper lad slumped and exhausted in a chair. "So how many sales did you make today?" The Boss asked expectantly.

"One." The lad replied.

"One?" The Boss said obviously displeased. "Most of the sales people on my staff make 20 or 30 sales a day. How much was the sale worth?"

"Exactly one hundred thousand, three hundred forty-three dollars and fifty-three cents." The lad said.

"How did you manage that?" The Boss asked flabbergasted.

"Well, this guy came in and I sold him a small fish hook, then a medium fish hook, and finally a really large hook. Then I sold him a small fishing line, a medium one, and a huge one. I asked him where he was going fishing, and he said he was going up to Oscoda to fish Lake Huron. I said he'd probably need a boat, so I took him down to the boat department and sold him the fancy 22-foot Chris Craft with twin engines. Then he said his Honda Civic probably wouldn't be able to handle the load, so I took him to the vehicle department and sold him a new GMC 1-ton pick-up truck."

"You sold all that to a guy who came in for a fish hook?" The Boss asked who couldn't believe what he just heard.

"He didn't come in for a fish hook," the Yooper lad explained, "He came in to buy a box of tampons for his wife, and I said to him, 'your weekend's shot. You might as well go fishing.'"

SPUD-NIK

Three dudes from Lower Michigan love to fish. So they decide they want to try ice fishing since they had heard so many good things to say about it. Since the ice was piss poor in Southern Michigan, the Three Amigos head up North, across the Big Mac Bridge to Yooperland. Once they get near the Little Bay De Noc River, they stop off at Bill's Bait Shop to get all their tackle and gear-including a spud to chop through the ice.

About two hours later, one of them was back at the Bait Shop and said to Bill, "We're going to need another spud." With a new spud in tow, the city slicker heads back out to his buddies on the ice. Another hour goes by, the same guy walks into Bill's again and says, "We're gonna need another spud." Well, Bill couldn't take it anymore, he needed to know.

"By the way," he says after selling the guy another spud, "How are you fellas doing out there?"

"Not very well at all," the Troll replies, "We don't even have the stupid boat in the water yet."

DY-NO-MITE!

Bitto Carlyson was the best fisherman in Tangle Town. He'd always come home with nice Brook Trout. No one could figure out where he was going to catch all those beauties. He finally asked me to go out with him one day as long as I didn't tell anyone where his spot was.

The next morning he picked me up and out North we went. We stopped at this bush road and he got out his pack sack and two plastic buckets. "Follow me." he says. We get to this beautiful pond and he reaches in his bag and takes out a stick of dynamite, lights it and heaves it out to the middle of the pond.

BOOM!

And a second later, a bunch of stunned Brook Trout float to the surface. "Let's fish,eh!" Bitto yells. We put all the trout in the two pails, still alive. We head back to truck with our booty and when we get there the Game Warden is waiting for us.

"Finally I got you!" The Game Warden says to Bitto, "Your a dead man."

"What do you mean?" Bitto asks.

"Well, I know damn well you don't have a fishing license and you're holding illegally caught fish. You're gonna hang."

"Wait a minute," Bitto replies, "Are you talking about these fish? These are my pet fish. I take 'em here so they can get some exercise and a little mating with the other Trout. When it's time to go, all I have to do is whistle and they jump back in buckets."

"Yah yah sure," the Warden says, "What a crock of bull that is. I've heard them all now! Let's go back to the pond, I gotta see this." So, we lug the two buckets of fish back to the pond and dump them back in. "Ok, Bitto, whistle and call them back. I want to see everyone of those fish jump back in the buckets." There was a long silence.

"What fish?" Bitto asks.

MAN WASN'T MEANT TO LIVE UP HERE IN THE WINTER

I ASKED Darb Holmgren one time what was the best time to disconnect the electric pump at the camp so it don't freeze up on me. Darb, being a Yooperland Guru, knew all things Yooper and told me that Labor Day was my best bet. You see, he knows the weather might either stay in the 80's from Labor Day until November or 2 days after Labor Day, drop down to the 20's and stay that way until next summer. That's why it's best to do everything by Labor Day, coz anytime after that is a gamble. You'd think after living up here all my life I would've used my Yooper instincts and did what Darb told me to do, but no. I'd rather play Yooper Roulette with the weather. It's more fun that way. Especially when your pump and water lines freeze up under the camp and you gotta crawl under there and hope none of the pipes burst. I've already cracked two pumps playing Yooper Roulette, procrastinating, hoping the weather was going to hold out just a few more weeks.

It's the same thing when it comes to long underwear. When the hell do you take those damn things off? Darb told me July 4th, but even that's a gamble. Don't laugh, this is true. One time, back in the 70's, a bunch of us guys decided to go up to Republic for the festivities they had every year for the 3rd and 4th of July. We entered a bunch of events like canoe races, tug of war, etc. and stayed in the cabins they had behind the Nature Bar. After a great party the night of the 3rd, we woke up the next morning to 30 degrees and a few feet of snow! Of course none of us thought to toss some warm clothes in the trunk like our moms always told us to, so there we were standing outside in our shorts drinking cold beer and eating pasties in the middle of a snowstorm! It was no fun at all.

Being a musician in Yooperland is the true test of your love of music. If you ever want to know when a big snow storm is going to hit, just check with Da Yoopers coz every time we gotta travel somewhere to play music, it's snows. I remember one time back in the 70's when we had a job down in Munising. The weather had been gorgeous right up through November. That particular day, it was in the 60's so we headed down there in our thin jackets, no boots, no shovel, no hat, no gloves, and no long underwear. We got down there, and after loading in, we parked the van in front of the bar and played the gig. By the time we went to load out, we couldn't find the van because there was a snowdrift from the bar roof all the way across the street! After tunneling the van out and starting home, it was a white out all the way back to Ishpeming. Visibility was about 2 feet in front of you and that was it. I had to drive, and by the end of the ride I had sore spots on my wrists and shoulders, from gripping the wheel so tight and from guys resting their chins on my shoulders and staring out into the black and white swirling abyss. What a hell ride that was.

All you have to do to get out of the winter weather up here is drive 3 hours south to Green Bay and you are in the tropics. If you are ever in Green Bay in the middle of winter, and you see someone on the side of the road on his hands and knees, they're probably not drunk, it's just a Yooper who hasn't seen black top for 6 months, so he's just checking it out to remember what it looks and feels like.

October 31st is the usual time the retired Yoopers from Yooperland head south to Arizona for the winter. No more snow shovels, snow scoops, snow plows, snow blowers, roof rakes, salt, frozen water lines, flooded basements and 40 below weather. I can't wait until the time I can jump in the van and head her down to the desert and dance around a cactus with a Corona.

Let's just face it, Man just wasn't meant to live up here in the winter.

THE MEANEST DOGS IN TANGLE TOWN

WHEN I was growing up back in the 50's, there were a lot of real mean dogs in town. Growling, snarling mean dogs with mean owners who beat them and kicked them around so they had no choice but to be nasty. Then there was the dogs who were just born mean, who had really nice owners who loved and cared for them, but would still lay in wait for us idiot kids to ride by and bite our asses off. In those days, us kids were fair game to anyone that was bigger and stronger than us, and the neighborhood dogs were no exception.

John Pete's Hill was our neighborhood hill where all the kids used to meet and ride our crates in the summer and our sleighs in the winter. It was real steep and had another hill on the other side that you would ride up at the end of your run. To the right of the hill lived this massive mean dark brown Collie looking thing, which would chase cars and kids. You'd be riding home on your bike from the hill and that bugger would fly out and grab the cuff of your pants and tear you off of your bike. You'd come home bleeding and limping, and the exchange between you and your mother would go something like this:

"Oh my god, I don't know what I'm gonna do with you... you ruined your pants again! Can't you learn to be more careful?" She would say.

"No, Ma, it's not my fault, I just got my ass chewed on by that lion that lives on John Pete's Hill." Sheesh, you'd get no sympathy from her!

Me, Etta Norman and Al Gustafson went to the Ridge Street School and on the way to school every morning, we had to pass this house that had this elephant sized Saint Bernard on a chain. I remember his head being as big as a boxcar! He would hide in the porch were we couldn't see him. Then, when we got even with the house we could hear those big huge paws of his pounding on the porch and cranking up to attack us. We soon learned after our first meeting with him where the end of his chain was, so every time after that, when we got close to the house, we'd slowly drift out to the middle of the street. One time we were making our usual trek out to the middle of the street, when we noticed that bighead was nowhere in sight. We thought we were free of him and he'd got run over by a car or something, but sure enough just as we passed by the house and started rounding the corner, he comes flying around the house from the backyard, sans chain. To say we took off like a bat out of Hell was an understatement. That dog chased us all the way to school and still to this day I can recall the feeling of his breath on my bum. Man what a scary thing for a kid to experience! You knew you couldn't outrun the dog, but that didn't matter. You just had to make sure to outrun both of your friends so they could be fresh meat for the dog and not you.

The Naults had this big mammoth of a sleigh dog. He was yellow, black, and big as a horse. You would ride by their house on your bike and that bugger would come flying out of the Lilac bushes and hit the end of his chain a foot from your left leg. He knocked many a poor kid off their bikes that were dumb enough to ride too close to those bushes. We always talked about putting an end to those scary animals coz every kid in the neighborhood was getting tired of being chewed on. The owners knew about what their dogs were doing and some of them got a kick out of it! We had this one bulldog that lived on the bottom of High Street Hill. It was on the way to

Charley Richard's store where we went for candy, pop, and chips. The old man and the bulldog would sit on the porch and wait for some dumb kid to come cruising by and he would sic the dog on you! That dog would jump up and hit you with his 2 front legs and knock you ass over tin cups. The old man would be sitting up there cackling like a crow!

REVENGE

One time I was pedaling by Nault's house preparing myself for the big yellow and black monster to come flying out of the bushes at me. He came out all right, but this time he wasn't on the chain. He sauntered out of the bushes and sat down right in my path staring me down, causing me to slam on my brakes. I froze in terror. The dog had this cocksure air about him, like a bully has when he knows he has you cornered. Big Ugly walks over to me and I mutter an "Oh shit" and use every ounce of self-control not to start screaming for my mother like a baby. He takes a sniff of my left leg and then circles around to the other side and sniffs my other leg. They say dogs can sense fear and I knew he could sense the waterfall of fear cascading off of me. He takes one more circle around me and stops right before my left leg, positions himself and lifts his hind leg, releasing a jet of whiz that covers the cuff of my pants, my sock and my shoe. Big ugly must've been saving up, coz it seemed like it took him a half hour to empty his tank. Then, as if that wasn't enough, when he was done, he moved forward a little and kicked some dirt at me with his back legs, and I swear as the bastard walked away he snickered at me! Well that was it. I went down and bought myself a pellet pistol with my life savings, and headed out for revenge. I grabbed Al Gustafson and had him steer and pedal my bike while I rode on the back fully armed with my new purchase. We rode as fast as we could towards Nault's and when we saw Jumbo come dashing out of the lilac bushes, I pulled out the gun and waited. When we got parallel with him and he was barking and leaping at us, I reached down and stuck the pistol right up his butt and fired. Oh the howl that came from that dog! After our vigilante work, he never chased another kid again. He was scraping his butt on the sidewalk for weeks. Old man Nault just thought he had worms.

We were on a roll. The mean ass bugger on John Pete's Hill got run over by some guy on a Harley, so we went after Mister Bulldog and His Cackling Buddy. We came whizzing down the hill, Al pumping as fast as his legs could. As before, I waited until the Bulldog was alongside us and I aimed right at his brown eye and Pow! One right up the butt. It was my signature move. He went howling back up to the porch, back up to the Cackler, who wasn't laughing anymore. Feeling confident after two "kills" we stopped the bike and announced to Old Cackler "Lone Ranger style" never to sic that dog at any kids again or the next time we'll go for his eyeballs! We became heroes of the neighborhood... everyone was talking about us. Word spread so fast that we started to get calls from kids in other neighborhoods, to help take care of their problem dogs, so we decided to rent ourselves for a quarter a pop. We ended up making a lot of money that summer!

Our biggest win though was over Zip Jocksey's dog, Butch. He was the meanest of them all. You know that saying "Dogs resemble their owners?" Well in this case it was true! He was an ugly, snarling, two hundred pound biting machine... Just like Zip. He would let Butch roam around freely, so there was no kid in the neighborhood that didn't tangle with him at one point or another. We lived in constant fear of being attacked by him. He used to grab you by the cuff of the pants or your shoe or anything you happened to wave at him to defend yourself, and proceed to drag you over rocks, gravel, dirt, mud puddles, etc. If he got tired he'd stop and put a paw on you to keep you down and once he was rested, he'd continue pulling you. All you could do in that situation was curl up in a ball and wait until he was done with you.

It was when Vito had gotten into a bad skiing accident and broke both his leg and his shoulder. He was hobbling home on his crutches one day, and he was just about home when he came upon Butch standing on a snow bank right next to Windsand's Paint Store. Vito tried to slink past Butch undetected, but to no avail. The moment Butch spotted him he dove on him from the top of the bank and knocked him for a loop. His crutches went flying one way and he went another. Without the crutches, Vito couldn't get up and was defenseless against Butch who tore him up pretty bad. Luckily, a car came by afterwards and scraped Vito up off the road and brought him home.

That night Vito called me with the fire of revenge in his heart. So we came up with a plan. We knew that every Friday night Zip and his wife would go to the IGA shopping and they would chain Butch up to the house. We also knew that Gary Sparks lived next door to Zip and always went to Woody's Bar every Friday night after supper. So one Friday night, we waited down the street for Zip and his wife to leave for the grocery store. Right on time we saw them pull out and head down the street, so we sprang into action. Vito stood in front of the house out in the road and yelled and screamed at Butch who was snarling and foaming at him, pulling his chain taut. Meanwhile I had a 50 foot hemp rope that we used for a Tarzan swing which I tied the one end to Gary Sparks Nash Rambler and lassoed Butch with the other end. Not five minutes later Gary comes out of the house like clockwork and cranks up the Nash Rambler. I then snuck behind Butch and unhooked his chain from the house and as soon as Gary peeled out and the rope went taut, away went Butch! We couldn't stay standing we were laughing so hard! Gary dragged Butch all over town and every kid who was out that night cheered. It was the perfect revenge for a dog that made a sport of dragging all the neighborhood kids around. People were talking about that one for months afterward.

Our glory didn't last long though. As a means to supplement my income from my "job" I used to collect empty pop bottles and return them to Charley Richard's store. So one day a few weeks into our vigilante work, still high from being a hero of the neighborhoods, I decided to take my stash back, two shopping bags full of heavy bottles, the ones I got a nickel for. Those bags felt like they weighed 50 lbs each. I was huffing and puffing along and was almost at Charley's when I got the uneasy feeling that something or someone was following me. I turned around and what do I see but Cackler's ugly bulldog staring me down. Off in the distance, I could hear the Old man cackling his head off. I tried inching away, but he was matching me step for step. I'd take a step back and he'd take a step forward. I knew I had to make a decision: Fight or Flight. Do I stand my ground and heave one of these coke bottles at his head? No he probably wouldn't feel it with a thick head like that and I'd just end up getting mauled. Flight was the best option, I had a good chance of making it to Charley's place before that bugger got me. So in the blink of an eye, I turned and tore off towards the store, losing my bottles left and right in the meantime. Once I was in earshot of the store, I started yelling to Charley to open the door, and by the time I reached it I had only a handful of bottles left. I always wondered, in the short time I was the Lone Ranger doling out justice to neighborhood dogs, does a mean old nasty dog remember who gave him a pain in his ass? Well, dear reader, I'm hear to say they are like elephants, at least that Bulldog was, coz I got the teeth marks on my bum to prove it...

Hoolie on stage: above & right

Hoolie & his alter ego, Harold

Hoolie in da studio

Below:
Hoolie & Bella, da songwriters

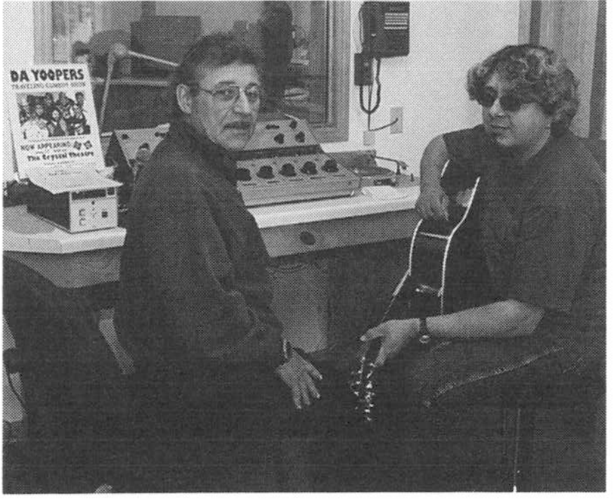